Statistical Concepts

STATISTICAL
CONCEPTS
A BASIC PROGRAM

JIMMY R. AMOS

FOSTER LLOYD BROWN

OSCAR G. MINK

HARPER & ROW, PUBLISHERS

NEW YORK, EVANSTON, AND LONDON

Contents

Preface   vii

Tips to the Student   viii

Frequency Distribution   1
   (1–9)

Averages   5
   (10–31)

Median   13
   (32–47)

Mode   20
   (48–59)

The Normal Curve   26
   (60–88)

Variability   39
   (89–111)

Interpreting Test Scores   47
   (112–134)

Standard Score   54
   (135–148)

Relationship: Correlation Coefficient   59
   (149–164)

Reliability and Validity   65
   (165–185)

Inferential Statistics   72
   (186–234)

Regression   92
   (235–253)

Standard Error of Measurement   101
   (254–263)

Diagnostic Test and Alphabetical Index   107

Evaluative Data   121

Preface

The beginning student in psychology, educational psychology, guidance, and similar fields in the behavioral sciences must gain a conceptual understanding of statistical procedures in order to read the experimental literature assigned for readings in most introductory courses.

This program was developed in an effort to assist our students in obtaining a conceptual understanding of certain statistical phenomena without sacrificing a week of class time presenting the material in lecture and discussion sections. Our reasons went beyond the desire to conserve class time for other introductory material however, as our experience with a large class of students with diverse abilities suggested that some were quick to grasp or already knew the basic statistical concepts. As a result, some students were easily bored, whereas others needed special review sessions. We believed that the ideal answer to our dilemma was completely individualized instruction. Our solution was programmed instruction. We searched for a usable program. To our dismay we could locate nothing that seemed appropriate; the programs were either too comprehensive—or too much like workbooks and programs in name only.

This program exposes the student to: (1) Descriptive statistics—central tendency, measures of variability, correlation, and the application of these concepts in the concepts of reliability, validity, and norming. (2) Inferential statistics—significance testing including analysis of variance.

The program can be completed in five hours by the typical beginning student. The program has been tested seven times for error rate and has been used in seven separate experimental studies. The evaluative data available suggests that the program is fulfilling its purpose. As you use this program, you will find that it contributes to your effectiveness as instructors and students. Many of you will have creative suggestions and constructive criticisms of value to the authors. We welcome such assistance and will embody the best suggestions in future editions.

JIMMY R. AMOS
FOSTER LLOYD BROWN
OSCAR G. MINK

Tips to the Student

There are no doubt some of you who are somewhat reluctant to study statistics because you have heard that it is difficult and highly technical. This text was carefully designed to present the material in small steps and to check your growing understanding at each step. Even the most mathematically inept should be able to understand and enjoy this book.

Try to respond correctly to each frame before you see the "book response." It will help you to avoid seeing the "book response" if you use a mask of paper or cardboard which you slide down the page as you progress. You can thus make sure that you understand each frame as it comes along. This is especially helpful when you are tired or preoccupied. A programmed text is well adapted to study in odd free moments that might otherwise be wasted. If you are a particularly busy person, you might wish to take advantage of this characteristic. The very best results will occur if you can give this text the same undivided attention you would give a classroom text.

Some of you will spend less than four and one-half hours working the program; but, you will have mastered some important concepts necessary in understanding today's research literature in the behavioral and social sciences.

Statistical Concepts

FREQUENCY DISTRIBUTION

1. Such things as test scores, class rank, weight, and income, are called variables. Income, for instance, is called a variable because different income values are possible. In general, things that vary in value from case to case or time to time are called

_____.

VARIABLES

2. The number of times a particular value of a variable occurs is referred to as the *frequency* of that value. If 17 students receive a score of 70 on a test, then the score of 70 has a _____ of 17.

FREQUENCY

3. A distribution is a series of separate values such as scores which are arranged or ordered according to magnitude. A group of ordered scores is a *distribution*. For example, a group of scores ranging from the lowest to the highest score is a _____ (see table).

Scores
13
11
11
9
9
9
8
5

DISTRIBUTION

4. A set of ordered scores and their corresponding frequencies is called a *frequency distribution*. This can be represented in table or graph form. The table below shows the number of times a score occurs in its group. This table is a frequency

——————————————.

Scores	Frequency
13	I
11	II
9	III
8	I
5	I

DISTRIBUTION

5. Frequency distributions can also be graphically illustrated. The two most common graphs used to illustrate frequency distributions are the *frequency polygon* and the *histogram*. If scores and their frequencies are illustrated with points connected by lines, it is called a *frequency polygon*. Because the illustration below shows the frequency of particular scores by the height of points that are connected by lines, it is called a frequency

——————————————.

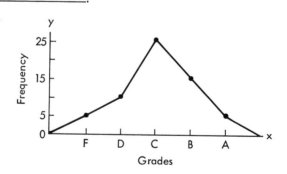

POLYGON

6. When a frequency distribution is illustrated in the form of a histogram, the scores and their frequencies are designated by rectangular boxes. In the frequency distribution below, the height of the rectangular boxes indicates the frequency with which students received particular scores. It is called a _____.

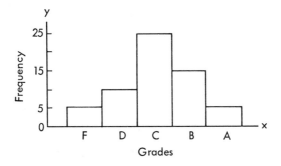

HISTOGRAM

7. It is the accepted practice for the vertical side of a graph, called the *ordinate* axis, to be used to designate the frequency. The horizontal side, called the *abscissa* axis, is used for the scores. Direction of increase is upward for the frequency on the ordinate axis. Direction of increase for the variable is from left to right on the _____ axis.

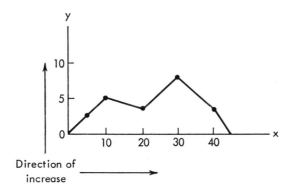

ABSCISSA

8. On this graph the *f*, which designates the frequency, is the
_____ axis, and the *x*, designating the variable, is
the _____ axis.

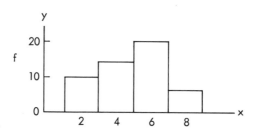

ORDINATE

ABSCISSA

9. The two most common graphs used to illustrate frequency distributions are the frequency polygon and the _____.
Graph A is a _____. Graph B is a _____
_____.

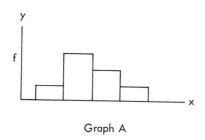 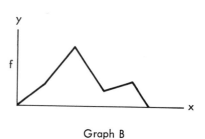

Graph A   Graph B

HISTOGRAM

HISTOGRAM

FREQUENCY POLYGON

AVERAGES

10. After scores have been tabulated into a frequency distribution, a measure of *central tendency,* or central position is often calculated. Central tendency gives us a concise description of the average or typical performance of the group as a whole. Measures of _____ tendency allow us to compare two or more groups in terms of typical performance.

:::

CENTRAL

11. In statistics there are several "averages" or measures of _____ _____ in common use. Three of these are: (a) the mean, (b) the median, and (c) the mode.

:::

CENTRAL TENDENCY

12. The mean is generally the most familiar and most useful to us. The mean is computed by dividing the *sum of the scores* by the *total number of scores.* The formula for the mean would be

$$\text{Mean} = \frac{\text{sum of the scores}}{?}.$$

:::

TOTAL NUMBER OF SCORES

13. Instead of stating that the mean is the sum of the scores divided by the total number of scores, it is easier to use the following symbols:
a. Mean $= \bar{X}$ (read "X bar") or M. (The symbol $\bar{X}$ or M is used when referring to the mean of a sample from the total population.)

b. Sum of the scores $= \Sigma X$ ($\Sigma =$ sum; $X =$ each score).

c. Total number of scores $= N$.

Thus the formula for the mean would be $\overline{X} = ?/?$

※※※※※※※※※※※※※※※※※※※※※※※※※※※※※※※※※

$$\Sigma X/N$$

14. Compute the mean ($\overline{X} = \Sigma X/N$) from the given information:

Scores (X):　　　　　　7

　　　　　　　　　　　3

　　　　　　　　　　　6

　　　　　　　　　　　4
　　　　　　　　　　　―

Sum of scores (ΣX):　20

Number of scores (N):　4

$\overline{X} = ?/? = ?$

※※※※※※※※※※※※※※※※※※※※※※※※※※※※※※※※※※※

$$20/4 = 5$$

15. Finding the arithmetic mean of a distribution is analogous to finding the center of moment, or the center of gravity, in a solid block. If a distribution were suspended by the mean it would hang level or balanced. The mean, whose symbol is ———,
is the center of gravity in a frequency distribution.

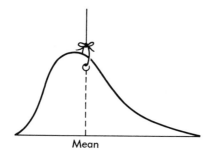

Mean

※※※※※※※※※※※※※※※※※※※※※※※※※※※※※※※※※

$$\overline{X} \text{ OR } M$$

16. Thus, if extremely high or extremely low scores are added to a distribution, the mean tends to shift toward those scores. If the center of gravity of the distribution is shifted to one side or the other of the curve, the curve becomes "skewed." The following curve has a few extremely low scores. Consequently, this distribution is _____.

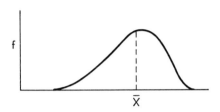

SKEWED

17. Extreme scores, either high or low, tend to _____ a distribution.

SKEW

18. If a distribution is massed so that the greatest number of scores is at the right end of the curve and a few scores are scattered at the left end, the curve is said to be *negatively* skewed. If the massing of scores is at the left end of the curve with the tail extending to the right end, then the curve is *positively* skewed.

Graph A illustrates _____ skewness. Graph B illustrates _____ skewness.

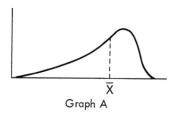 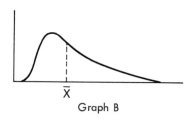

Graph A   Graph B

❋❋❋❋❋❋❋❋❋❋❋❋❋❋❋❋❋❋❋❋❋❋❋❋❋❋❋❋❋❋❋❋❋❋❋

NEGATIVE

❋❋❋❋❋❋❋❋❋❋❋❋❋❋❋❋❋❋❋❋❋❋❋❋❋❋❋❋❋❋❋❋❋❋❋

POSITIVE

19. This graph's tail is extending to the right because of a few extremely high scores and is therefore _____ skewed.

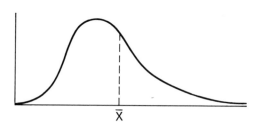

❋❋❋❋❋❋❋❋❋❋❋❋❋❋❋❋❋❋❋❋❋❋❋❋❋❋❋❋❋❋❋❋❋❋❋

POSITIVELY

20. A curve is *symmetrical* when one half of the curve is a mirror image of the other half. If you folded a frequency polygon

at the mean and the two halves were similar, then the frequency distribution represented by the polygon would be said to be

_____.

✽✽✽✽✽✽✽✽✽✽✽✽✽✽✽✽✽✽✽✽✽✽✽✽✽✽✽✽✽✽✽✽✽✽

SYMMETRICAL

21. According to the formula for computing the mean ($\overline{X} = \Sigma X/N$), we can define the mean as the arithmetic average of the scores in a distribution. If we added extreme scores to one end of a previously symmetrical curve, the mean would shift towards those extreme scores. Would the curve be symmetrical or not symmetrical? _____

✽✽✽✽✽✽✽✽✽✽✽✽✽✽✽✽✽✽✽✽✽✽✽✽✽✽✽✽✽✽✽✽✽✽

NOT SYMMETRICAL (OR ASYMMETRICAL)

22. Regardless of whether the curve is symmetrical or asymmetrical, the mean is always the center of balance. Does this imply that the mean is always centrally located in asymmetrical curves?

_____

✽✽✽✽✽✽✽✽✽✽✽✽✽✽✽✽✽✽✽✽✽✽✽✽✽✽✽✽✽✽✽✽✽✽

NO

23. Let us illustrate this point by placing a distribution along an interval scale such as that below. Each figure represents one person. The scale would obviously balance if a fulcrum were

under the middle number, 4. To verify this, calculate the mean by the formula $\bar{X} = \Sigma X/N$. Was this distribution symmetrical?

_____

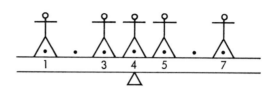

****

$$\bar{X} = 20/5 = 4$$

****

YES

24. If the person with a score of 7 had scored 12, what would be the mean? _____ Place a fulcrum (i.e., △) at the balance point of the scale below. Is the fulcrum centrally located? _____ Is this distribution symmetrical?

_____

****

5

****

FULCRUM SHOULD BE UNDER NUMBER 5

****

NO

****

NO

25. What would be the mean for the above distribution if the person who scored 12 had instead scored 22? _____

✻✻✻✻✻✻✻✻✻✻✻✻✻✻✻✻✻✻✻✻✻✻✻✻✻✻✻✻✻✻✻✻

7

26. When a curve is positively skewed (see graph A) the mean is located to the _____ (right or left) of most of the cases. When a curve is negatively skewed (see graph B) the mean is located to the _____ of most of the cases. (Each dot is one case.)

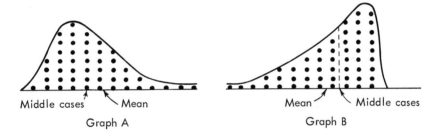

✻✻✻✻✻✻✻✻✻✻✻✻✻✻✻✻✻✻✻✻✻✻✻✻✻✻✻✻✻✻✻✻

RIGHT

✻✻✻✻✻✻✻✻✻✻✻✻✻✻✻✻✻✻✻✻✻✻✻✻✻✻✻✻✻✻✻✻

LEFT

27. If the measures 2, 2, 3, 3, 15 were a frequency distribution, the curve would be _____ skewed.

✻✻✻✻✻✻✻✻✻✻✻✻✻✻✻✻✻✻✻✻✻✻✻✻✻✻✻✻✻✻✻✻

POSITIVELY

28. The preceding distribution of 2, 2, 3, 3, 15 has a mean of 5. What will the mean be if 10 points are added to the score of 15 (making it a score of 25)? _____

✻✻✻✻✻✻✻✻✻✻✻✻✻✻✻✻✻✻✻✻✻✻✻✻✻✻✻✻✻✻✻
7

29. We saw that by adding 10 points to the score of 15, the mean of the distribution 2, 2, 3, 3, 15 was raised by 2 points. The reason for this is that the mean is an arithmetic average and each score contributes to its value. When 10 was added it was averaged or distributed equally among the five scores. This has the same effect as adding a constant of 2 points to each score (10 points/5 scores = 2 points per score). When 2 points are added to each score, the mean is raised by _____ points (from 5 to 7).

✻✻✻✻✻✻✻✻✻✻✻✻✻✻✻✻✻✻✻✻✻✻✻✻✻✻✻✻✻✻✻
2

30. When a constant is added to each score of a distribution, that constant is added to the previous mean to find the new mean. If each score of a distribution is *multiplied* by a constant, the new mean is found by multiplying the old mean by that _____ _____.

✻✻✻✻✻✻✻✻✻✻✻✻✻✻✻✻✻✻✻✻✻✻✻✻✻✻✻✻✻✻✻
CONSTANT

31. The distribution 0, 2, 2, 3, 13 has a mean of 4. What would the mean be if each score was *multiplied* by a constant of 2? _____

✻✻✻✻✻✻✻✻✻✻✻✻✻✻✻✻✻✻✻✻✻✻✻✻✻✻✻✻✻✻✻
8

MEDIAN

32. By adding or substituting an extreme score to a distribution, the mean no longer represents a centrally located score but represents a measure that is more typical of the extreme score.

This causes us to rely on another measure of central tendency which is called the median or the middle score. The median is abbreviated Md or Mdn. The measure of central tendency that is less affected by the addition of an extreme score is the

_____.

MEDIAN

33. The median is a *point* on a scale of measurement above which are exactly half the cases and below which are the other half of the cases. The student should note that the median is defined as a *point* and not as a specific measurement, e.g., a score or a case. From the distribution 4, 6, 8, 10, 12, it is easy to see that 8 is the middle score. The score of 8 is at the *point* where there are two scores above and two scores below, hence, 8 is the median. What is the median of 11, 11, 14, 19, 19? _____

14

34. To obtain the median, the measures are arranged in ascending order from the lowest to the highest measure. Then by count-

ing up this scale, the point is selected above and below which there are an equal number of cases. The value of this point is the middle or the _____ case.

✻✻✻✻✻✻✻✻✻✻✻✻✻✻✻✻✻✻✻✻✻✻✻✻✻✻✻✻✻✻✻✻✻✻

MEDIAN

35. The median of the distribution 3, 2, 0, 1, 6 can be found by first arranging the measures from the lowest to the _____ number (0, 1, 2, 3, 6). Then we find the middle score or case, which is _____, and that is the median.

✻✻✻✻✻✻✻✻✻✻✻✻✻✻✻✻✻✻✻✻✻✻✻✻✻✻✻✻✻✻✻✻✻✻

HIGHEST

✻✻✻✻✻✻✻✻✻✻✻✻✻✻✻✻✻✻✻✻✻✻✻✻✻✻✻✻✻✻✻✻✻✻

2

36. It is not too difficult to determine the median of a distribution with an odd number of cases, provided the score at the midpoint has a frequency of 1. In the distribution 3, 5, 7, 9, 11, 13, 13, the median score, which is _____, has a frequency of 1. The score of 13 has a frequency of _____ _____.

✻✻✻✻✻✻✻✻✻✻✻✻✻✻✻✻✻✻✻✻✻✻✻✻✻✻✻✻✻✻✻✻✻✻

9

✻✻✻✻✻✻✻✻✻✻✻✻✻✻✻✻✻✻✻✻✻✻✻✻✻✻✻✻✻✻✻✻✻✻

2

37. A distribution whose midpoint score has a frequency greater than 1 (e.g., 5, 6, 9, 9, 9) presents a special problem. To overcome this, the student needs to know what is meant by "the interval of a score." For our purposes, the interval of a score ranges from .5 unit below a given score up to .5 unit above a given score. For example, the score of 9 includes all values within the limits of 8.5 up to 9.5. The exact midpoint of the interval whose lower and upper limits are 8.5 and 9.5, respectively, is 9. The score of 17 would represent the interval from 16.5 up to _____.

17.5

38. In the distribution of 5, 6, 6, 7, 8, 8, 8, 11, 13, 15, the score of 8 has a frequency of _____. The score of 8 has an interval range from 7.5 up to _____. It is assumed that the unit of three scores (8, 8, 8) is spread equally through the interval of 7.5 to 8.5. Each 8 occupies ⅓ (0.333) of a unit. For example:

3

8.5

39. The midpoint of the distribution 5, 6, 6, 7, 8, 8, 8, 11, 13, 15, where half the scores are on one side and half the scores are on the other, is between the fifth and _____ score. Below the interval 7.5 to 8.5 there are four scores, consequently the fifth score extends $\frac{1}{3}$ of the way into the three score unit. Thus, the point between the fifth score and the sixth, which is the _____, is found by adding $\frac{1}{3}$ of the unit to 7.5 ($7.5 + .33\frac{1}{3} = 7.83\frac{1}{3}$). Note the illustration:

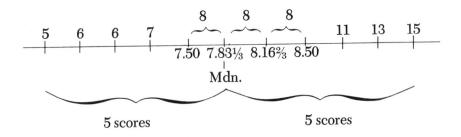

40. The distribution 1, 2, 2, 3, 3, 3, 3, 5, 6 has nine cases. The median of these nine cases is a point which has 4.5 cases below it and _____ cases above it. This midpoint falls within a four-case unit. Below the lower limit of 3 (which is 2.5) there are three cases; therefore by extending one and one-half cases into the interval of 2.5 to 3.5 we can locate the median. Each 3 accounts for one-fourth of the four-case unit, hence one and one-half cases is equal to $\frac{1}{4}$ plus $\frac{1}{8}$ of a unit ($0.25 + 0.12\frac{1}{2}$). The

value of the median is 2.5 + 0.37½ = _____. It is illustrated as follows:

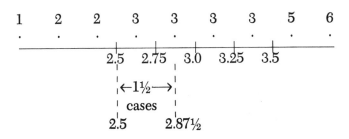

4.5

2.87½

41. The same principle applies to distributions with even numbers of cases except that the median falls midway between the two middle cases. For example in distribution A, shown below, the arrow indicates the median. Draw an arrow to indicate the median of distribution B.

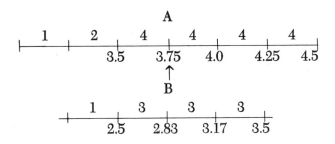

2.83

42. The distribution 40, 43, 44, 45, 48, 53, 56, 60 has eight cases. The median is a point midway between the fourth and _____

scores. The upper limit of 45 (the fourth score) is 45.5 and the lower limit of 48 (the fifth score) is _____ and midway between these two limits is the point 46.5, which is the median (as noted in the illustration below).

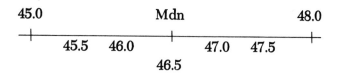

FIFTH

47.5

43. The distribution 10, 12, 14, 15 has four cases. The median is a point midway between the second and _____ case. The upper limit of 12 is _____, and the lower limit of 14 is _____. Midway between these two limits is the point _____, which is the median. Note the illustration:

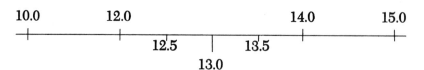

THIRD

12.5

13.5

13

44. The use of the median as an indicator of central tendency is increased when the end score is extreme. For example, the median of 0, 6, 9, 10, 10 is _____. The mean of this distribution is 7 (i.e., 35/5). If the extreme number 55 is substituted for one of the 10's, giving the distribution: 0, 6, 9, 10, 55, the median remains _____ but the mean is now _____.

✹✹✹✹✹✹✹✹✹✹✹✹✹✹✹✹✹✹✹✹✹✹✹✹✹✹✹✹✹✹✹✹✹

9

✹✹✹✹✹✹✹✹✹✹✹✹✹✹✹✹✹✹✹✹✹✹✹✹✹✹✹✹✹✹✹✹✹

9

✹✹✹✹✹✹✹✹✹✹✹✹✹✹✹✹✹✹✹✹✹✹✹✹✹✹✹✹✹✹✹✹✹

16

45. The mean and median will *both* be affected if the score of 55 is *added* to the distribution 0, 6, 9, 10, 10. The new distribution would be 0, 6, 9, 10, 10, 55. The mean is 90/6 = 15. The addition of the extreme score shifted the value of the mean 8 points to the right. How far to the right was the median shifted? _____ Which measure of central tendency was affected the least? _____

✹✹✹✹✹✹✹✹✹✹✹✹✹✹✹✹✹✹✹✹✹✹✹✹✹✹✹✹✹✹✹✹✹

.5 OR ONE-HALF OF A POINT

✹✹✹✹✹✹✹✹✹✹✹✹✹✹✹✹✹✹✹✹✹✹✹✹✹✹✹✹✹✹✹✹✹

MEDIAN

46. When we want to minimize the effect of one or more extreme scores, we should use the _____ to represent the average score of the distribution.

✻✻✻✻✻✻✻✻✻✻✻✻✻✻✻✻✻✻✻✻✻✻✻✻✻✻✻✻✻✻✻

MEDIAN

47. The median, for both odd and even number of cases, is the point on a distribution where there are an equal number of cases above and _____ that point.

✻✻✻✻✻✻✻✻✻✻✻✻✻✻✻✻✻✻✻✻✻✻✻✻✻✻✻✻✻✻✻

BELOW

MODE

48. A third measure of central tendency is the mode. It may be defined as the one value or score which occurs with the most frequency. The mode of the series 2, 3, 4, 4, 4, 5, 5 is 4. The mode of the series 7, 8, 10, 10, 10, 11, 11 is _____. The median is _____.

✻✻✻✻✻✻✻✻✻✻✻✻✻✻✻✻✻✻✻✻✻✻✻✻✻✻✻✻✻✻✻

10

✻✻✻✻✻✻✻✻✻✻✻✻✻✻✻✻✻✻✻✻✻✻✻✻✻✻✻✻✻✻✻

10

49. Is it possible for a distribution to have a median and a mode of the same value? _____ (yes or no)

❊❊❊❊❊❊❊❊❊❊❊❊❊❊❊❊❊❊❊❊❊❊❊❊❊❊❊❊❊❊❊❊❊❊

YES

50. The mode is used as a simple, inspectional "average" to show, quickly, the center of concentration of a frequency distribution. What is the mode or the rough average of the frequency distribution shown below? _____

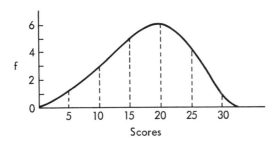

❊❊❊❊❊❊❊❊❊❊❊❊❊❊❊❊❊❊❊❊❊❊❊❊❊❊❊❊❊❊❊❊❊❊

20

51. The mode is not generally used unless there are a large number of cases in a distribution. When the number of cases in a distribution is small, it is more likely that several scores will have the same frequency. The frequency polygon shown below is an extreme example. It is evident that the mode is 10 but it does not give a close approximation of the average case. The mean is 25 ($\Sigma X/N = 125/5$). The cases, in ascending order, are

10, 10, 25, 35, 45, with the number 25 at the midpoint; thus
_____ is the median.

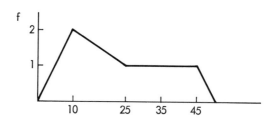

⁎⁎

25

52. The mode is used, in preference to either the median or the mean, when a measure of the most characteristic value of a group is desired. What is meant by "the most characteristic value" can be exemplified by clothing fashions. The _____ is what is being worn the most.

⁎⁎

MODE

53. The mode is used also to be sure that the average you obtain exists in actuality. In finding the average size of automobile tire that is purchased, the mean or median size might be a tire that doesn't exist. Therefore, one would want to know the size of tire bought most often. This would be the _____.

⁎⁎

MODE

54. In addition to serving as a measure of central tendency, the concept of modality is useful in describing the shape of some distributions. If a histogram or a frequency distribution has two peaks, it is referred to as a *bimodal* distribution. If a distribution has more than two peaks, it is called *multimodal*. The

following histogram appears to have two separate concentrations of frequencies; consequently it can be described as
_____ .

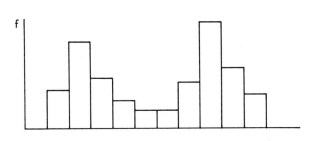

BIMODAL

55. The shape of the frequency distribution illustrated below is
_____ . The distribution of the histogram is
_____ . The frequency pologon is negatively skewed,
whereas the histogram is _____ skewed.

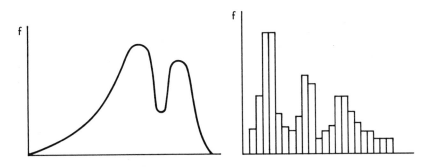

BIMODAL

MULTIMODAL

POSITIVELY

56. The score which occurs with the most frequency is the mode; hence the mode is totally uninfluenced by extreme scores. The mean is greatly influenced by extreme scores. On the basis of these two statements and the preceding exercises on the median, it is evident that line A indicates the mode since it is not influenced by the extreme scores. Line B is not affected as much as line C, thus it must be the _____. Line C is the _____; it was influenced the most by the extreme scores.

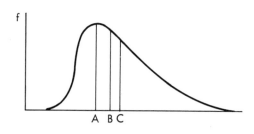

A B C

❋❋❋❋❋❋❋❋❋❋❋❋❋❋❋❋❋❋❋❋❋❋❋❋❋❋❋❋❋❋❋❋❋❋❋❋❋❋❋

MEDIAN

❋❋❋❋❋❋❋❋❋❋❋❋❋❋❋❋❋❋❋❋❋❋❋❋❋❋❋❋❋❋❋❋❋❋❋❋❋❋❋

MEAN

57. The frequency distribution below is _____ skewed. Line A indicates the _____. Line B indicates the _____. Line C indicates the _____. The mean of a negatively skewed distribution is located left of

the mode. The mean of a positively skewed distribution is located _____ of the center.

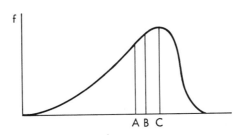

A B C

✻✻✻✻✻✻✻✻✻✻✻✻✻✻✻✻✻✻✻✻✻✻✻✻✻✻✻✻✻✻✻✻✻

NEGATIVELY

✻✻✻✻✻✻✻✻✻✻✻✻✻✻✻✻✻✻✻✻✻✻✻✻✻✻✻✻✻✻✻✻✻

MEAN

✻✻✻✻✻✻✻✻✻✻✻✻✻✻✻✻✻✻✻✻✻✻✻✻✻✻✻✻✻✻✻✻✻

MEDIAN

✻✻✻✻✻✻✻✻✻✻✻✻✻✻✻✻✻✻✻✻✻✻✻✻✻✻✻✻✻✻✻✻✻

MODE

✻✻✻✻✻✻✻✻✻✻✻✻✻✻✻✻✻✻✻✻✻✻✻✻✻✻✻✻✻✻✻✻✻

RIGHT

58. What are the mean, median, and mode of this distribution?

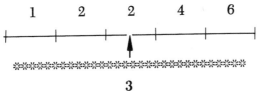

1   2   2   4   6

✻✻✻✻✻✻✻✻✻✻✻✻✻✻✻✻✻✻✻✻✻✻✻✻✻✻✻✻✻✻✻✻✻

3

✻✻✻✻✻✻✻✻✻✻✻✻✻✻✻✻✻✻✻✻✻✻✻✻✻✻✻✻✻✻✻✻✻

2.25

✻✻✻✻✻✻✻✻✻✻✻✻✻✻✻✻✻✻✻✻✻✻✻✻✻✻✻✻✻✻✻✻✻

2

59. The mean, median, and mode have been discussed as averages. It should now be evident why these three statistical tools are called measures of _____.

✶✶✶✶✶✶✶✶✶✶✶✶✶✶✶✶✶✶✶✶✶✶✶✶✶✶✶✶✶✶✶✶

CENTRAL TENDENCY

THE NORMAL CURVE

60. Let us suppose that each of 260 students lined up in front of signs according to weights. The signs run from left-to-right in order of increasing weight from 135 to 165 pounds. The number of persons in any one line is the frequency of that weight. The number of 150 pounders is the _____ of 150 pounders.

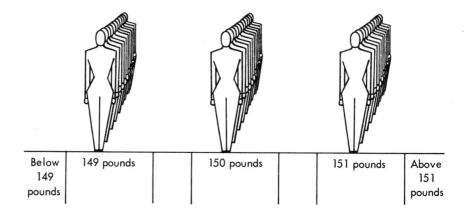

| Below 149 pounds | 149 pounds | | 150 pounds | | 151 pounds | Above 151 pounds |

✶✶✶✶✶✶✶✶✶✶✶✶✶✶✶✶✶✶✶✶✶✶✶✶✶✶✶✶✶✶✶✶

FREQUENCY

61. From an airplane, the place where this odd event was occurring might look like the diagram below. Each dot represents a
_____.

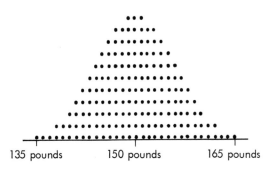

135 pounds   150 pounds   165 pounds

PERSON OR STUDENT

62. Assuming that the students are separated from one another by the same amount of space, the *number of cases would be indicated by the area*. For example with 260 cases, the 26 heaviest students would occupy the extreme right 10% of the crowd. The 13 lightest people would occupy the extreme left _____ _____% of the crowd.

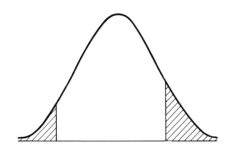

5%

63. If each column of students is represented by a rectangular box, we have our old friend the _____.

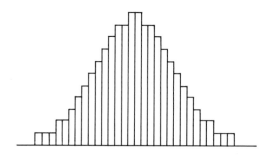

HISTOGRAM

64. If we have a very large number of people and use very small weight categories, the irregular step-like curve would become smooth and continuous. The resulting figure approaches a special type of curve called the normal curve. In frequency distributions normality is not associated with small groups of people but rather with very _____ groups of people.

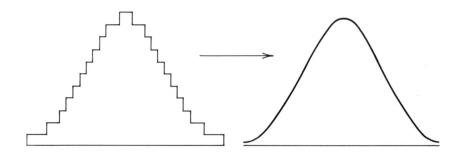

LARGE

65. In a normal curve (which by definition describes an infinite number of cases) the tails of the curve never touch the baseline. Which curve below could be a true normal curve? _____.

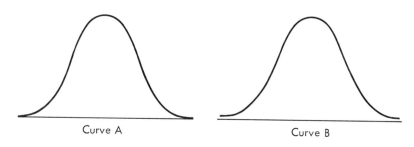

Curve A   Curve B

❋❋❋❋❋❋❋❋❋❋❋❋❋❋❋❋❋❋❋❋❋❋❋❋❋❋❋❋❋❋❋❋❋❋

B

66. It has been found that quantitative data gathered about a variety of natural phenomena, including many mental and social traits, form distributions, that though not precisely normal in distribution, may be closely described by the normal _____.

❋❋❋❋❋❋❋❋❋❋❋❋❋❋❋❋❋❋❋❋❋❋❋❋❋❋❋❋❋❋❋❋❋❋

CURVE

67. The distributions of such diverse properties as achievement test scores, I. Q., and height and weight of people form approximately _____ _____.

❋❋❋❋❋❋❋❋❋❋❋❋❋❋❋❋❋❋❋❋❋❋❋❋❋❋❋❋❋❋❋❋❋❋

NORMAL CURVES

68. The tails of a normal curve recede indefinitely and never touch the abscissa or base line because the number of cases needed to form a normal curve is _____.

❋❋❋❋❋❋❋❋❋❋❋❋❋❋❋❋❋❋❋❋❋❋❋❋❋❋❋❋❋❋❋❋❋❋

INFINITE

69. When a line approaches infinitely closely to another line but does not touch that line, the lines are said to be asymptotic. The tails of a normal curve are _____ to the base line.

ASYMPTOTIC

70. The bell-shaped curve illustrated below approximates what the statisticians call a normal curve. Note the following properties:
    a. It is symmetrical.
    b. The mean, median, and mode have the same value (in this instance, 70).
    c. There are thus an equal number of scores on either side of the mean (central axis).
    d. It is composed of infinitely large numbers of _____.
    e. The tails of the curve are _____ to the abscissa (base line).

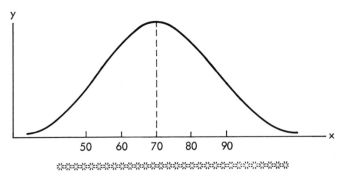

CASES

ASYMPTOTIC

71. Another identifying characteristic of the normal curve is its mathematical construction. There are two points on the normal

curve where the curve changes direction from convex to con-
cave. These points are points of inflection (see graph A). Are the
inflection points on graph B at lines W, lines X, or lines Y?

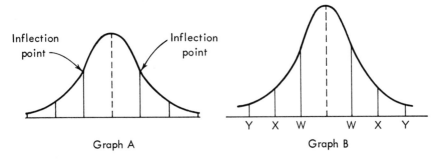

Graph A   Graph B

LINE **W**

72. Perpendicular lines drawn from the abscissa to the points of inflection may be regarded as marking off *one unit* of distance or
deviation from the mean (or central axis). If one uses this distance as a *standard,* a uniform method of dividing the base line
into equal segments can be established. If the central axis is
designated as zero, the line one unit of distance to the right
would be plus one and the line one unit of distance to the left
would be ＿＿＿＿＿＿＿＿＿ ＿＿＿＿＿＿＿＿＿.

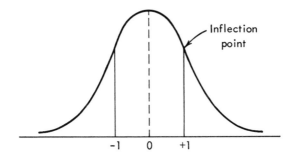

MINUS ONE

73. Mathematically, the points -1 and $+1$ are situated one unit of distance or deviation from the central axis or values (the mean, median, and mode). These two points are designated as ± 1 (read as plus and minus one). Two units of distance or deviation from the central axis are labeled as $+2$ and _____.

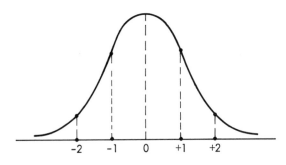

-2

74. Using the unit of distance established by constructing a perpendicular line from the point of inflection to the abscissa as a standard, we can divide the base line into several equal segments. Since the normal curve is asymptotic with respect to the abscissa, one could divide the base line into equal parts indefinitely. All segments would be a uniform or standard distance. The unit of distance was established by constructing a perpendicular line from the point of _____ to the abscissa.

INFLECTION

75. The proportion of cases beyond ± 3 units from the center of the normal curve is so small that they are generally ignored. It is thus common practice to illustrate only those cases contained between the arbitrary limits of $+3$ and _____ units of deviation.

-3

33

76. Notice that in the graph below each divided segment is equal to the distance from (or the deviation from) the mean to the perpendicular line drawn from the _____ point.

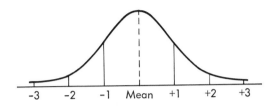

INFLECTION

77. The total area under the normal curve may be set to equal 1 or unity. Between the mean and +1 unit of deviation to the right of the mean is .3413 of the total area. Thus the area from the mean to +1 unit of deviation contains 34.13% of the total cases. Since −1 unit of deviation is equal in area to +1 unit of deviation, _____% of the total cases lie in the area between −1 unit of deviation and the mean.

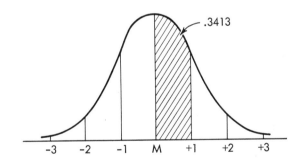

34.13

78. The symmetry and massing of scores around the central values groups little more than ⅔ (2 × 34.13% = 68.26%) of the total frequencies between +1 and −1 deviations. If a normal distri-

bution has a total frequency of 1000 scores, approximately 341 scores (34.13% × 1000) are located between the mean and −1 unit of deviation and approximately 341 scores are located between the mean and +1 unit of deviation. How many scores are located between −1 deviation and +1 unit of deviation?

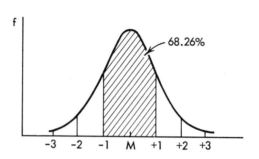

683 (682.6)

79. In this frequency distribution the deviation points, −1 and +1, mark off the middle _____% of the total scores. They occur at the scores of 40 and _____.

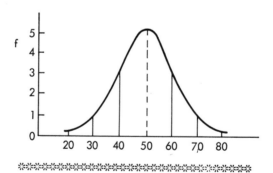

68.26 OR 68

60

80. Although the normal curve extends indefinitely to the left and to the right, the end points of the curve approach the base line so

closely that over 95.44% (see graph below) of the area or frequencies are included between the limits −2 and +2 and
99.74% of the cases are included between the limits −_____
and + _____.

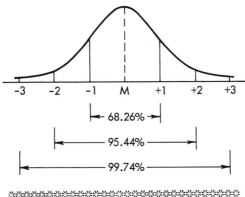

−3 AND +3

81. The percentage of cases contained between the mean (central
axis) of a normal curve and +3 units of deviation is 49.87%
(one-half of 99.74%). The percentage of cases between the central axis (the mean) of a normal curve and −2 units of deviation is _____%

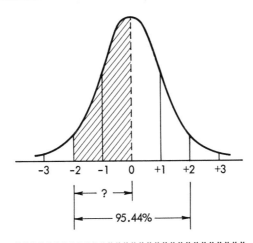

47.72

82. As we stated before, for practical purposes the limits of the frequencies of the normal curve rarely exceed those of ±3 units of deviation from the mean. The approximate twenty-six-hundredths of one percent (.0026) of the total cases occurring outside the limits of ±3 is so slight that unity is generally assumed to be within these limits. Approximately thirteen hundredths of one percent (.0013) of the total cases extend beyond +3 and approximately _____ hundredths of one percent of the total cases extend beyond −3.

THIRTEEN

83. Though the percentage of cases is very small and insignificant at a considerable distance from the mean (beyond ±3) the proportion of frequencies approaches zero but never equals zero. The reason is that the normal curve is _____ with respect to the abscissa or base line.

ASYMPTOTIC

84. Since the proportion of the total cases that exist beyond the limits of ±3 is so slight, it may be plausible to treat data as if 100% of the total cases fall within ±3 deviations. If one makes this assumption, the percentage of cases is rounded off to the nearest whole percent. Thus (note graph below) the percentages of cases from the mean to +1, +2, and +3 are 34%, 48%, and 50%, respectively. The percentages of cases *from the mean* to

−1, −2, and −3 deviations are _____%, _____%, and _____%, respectively.

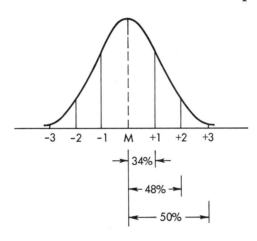

****

34

****

48

****

50

85. The percentage of cases below the mean is _____%.

****

50

86. The percentage of cases between the mean and +1 is _____%
of the total cases.

****

34

38

87. The percentage of cases below +1 deviation is 84% (50% plus 34%) of the total cases and the percentage of cases above +1 deviation is _____% of the total cases. The percentage of cases below −1 deviation is _____%.

❋❋❋❋❋❋❋❋❋❋❋❋❋❋❋❋❋❋❋❋❋❋❋❋❋❋❋❋❋

16 (100 − 84)

❋❋❋❋❋❋❋❋❋❋❋❋❋❋❋❋❋❋❋❋❋❋❋❋❋❋❋❋❋

16 (50 − 34)

88. In relation to the scores on the graph below, about what percentage of cases lie below 43? _____ Between 43 and 57? _____ Below 57? _____ Above 57? _____ Below 29? _____

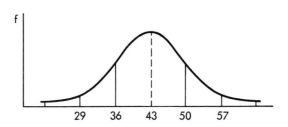

❋❋❋❋❋❋❋❋❋❋❋❋❋❋❋❋❋❋❋❋❋❋❋❋❋❋❋❋❋

50

❋❋❋❋❋❋❋❋❋❋❋❋❋❋❋❋❋❋❋❋❋❋❋❋❋❋❋❋❋

48

❋❋❋❋❋❋❋❋❋❋❋❋❋❋❋❋❋❋❋❋❋❋❋❋❋❋❋❋❋

98

❋❋❋❋❋❋❋❋❋❋❋❋❋❋❋❋❋❋❋❋❋❋❋❋❋❋❋❋❋

2

❋❋❋❋❋❋❋❋❋❋❋❋❋❋❋❋❋❋❋❋❋❋❋❋❋❋❋❋❋

2

VARIABILITY

89. Descriptions of groups by frequency distributions, central tendency, and normality have been discussed. Another way of describing a group is to have some index of how much variability exists. Consider the height of the two groups of people below. Both groups have a mean and median of 6 feet but the more variable is group _____.

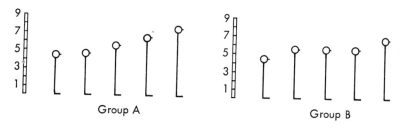

A

90. One common measure of variability is the range. The range of a set of scores is the distance between the midpoints of the lowest and highest scores. To find the range, subtract the lowest score from the highest score. The range of group A with heights of 4½, 5, 6, 7, 7½ is 7½ minus 4½ or 3. The range for the less variable group B with heights of 5, 6, 6, 6, 7 is _____.

2 (OR 7 MINUS 5)

91. If the normal curves below, in which the vertical deviation lines are one standard unit apart, represent large populations,

which curve represents the most variable group? _____

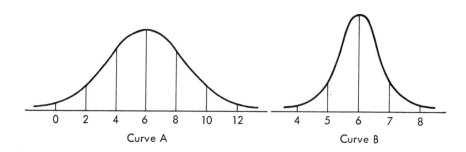

Curve A   Curve B

✻✻✻✻✻✻✻✻✻✻✻✻✻✻✻✻✻✻✻✻✻✻✻✻✻✻✻✻✻✻✻

CURVE A

92. The distance from one deviation point to the next is the other major index of variability. It is called a *standard deviation*. In the diagram below, 29 differs from 43 by two _____

_____.

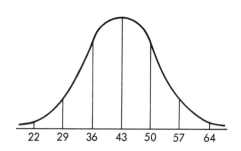

✻✻✻✻✻✻✻✻✻✻✻✻✻✻✻✻✻✻✻✻✻✻✻✻✻✻✻✻✻✻✻

STANDARD DEVIATIONS

93. When members of a group deviate very little from each other, the standard deviation is very small. The reverse is true for

highly variable groups. Consequently, the variability or diversity of two groups can be compared by the relative size of their _____ _____.

❉❉❉❉❉❉❉❉❉❉❉❉❉❉❉❉❉❉❉❉❉❉❉❉❉❉❉❉❉❉❉❉❉❉

STANDARD DEVIATIONS

94. The capital letters S.D. are used when referring to the standard deviation of a sample of a population. It is common practice to symbolize the standard deviation by the small Greek letter sigma (σ) when referring to the population values. To abbreviate a sample's standard deviation, one could use the capital letters _____. To abbreviate the standard deviation for a population, use the small Greek letter _____.

❉❉❉❉❉❉❉❉❉❉❉❉❉❉❉❉❉❉❉❉❉❉❉❉❉❉❉❉❉❉❉❉❉❉

S.D.

❉❉❉❉❉❉❉❉❉❉❉❉❉❉❉❉❉❉❉❉❉❉❉❉❉❉❉❉❉❉❉❉❉❉

σ OR SIGMA

95. Suppose that a population of scores is distributed so that the mean is 40 and the distance of 12 points is 1σ (read as one standard deviation). The students one standard deviation above the mean received the score of _____.

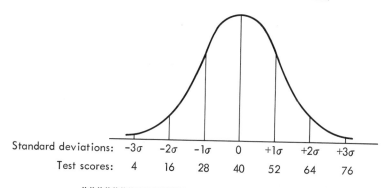

Standard deviations:	-3σ	-2σ	-1σ	0	$+1\sigma$	$+2\sigma$	$+3\sigma$
Test scores:	4	16	28	40	52	64	76

❉❉❉❉❉❉❉❉❉❉❉❉❉❉❉❉❉❉❉❉❉❉❉❉❉❉❉❉❉❉❉❉❉❉

96. What is the difference, in score points, between the scores of $+1\sigma$ and -2σ of the above illustration? _____

---

36 (3 × 12)

97. The standard deviation is a kind of average of all the deviations from the mean score. The amount a score (X) deviates from the mean ($\overline{X}$) is symbolized by the small letter x, that is, $X - \overline{X} = x$. Give the symbols for the following:

Raw score _____

Mean _____

Deviation _____

X

$\overline{X}$

---

x

98. To calculate a standard deviation, the deviations from the mean have to be squared. To square a number, you multiply it by itself. For example, 5 squared, or 5^2, $= 5 \times 5 = 25$; $2^2 =$ ____.

4

99. A minus times a minus equals a plus, therefore, $(-4)^2$ or $-4 \times -4 = 16$. Complete the following:

$$(-7)^2 = \underline{\hspace{3cm}}$$
$$(-3)^2 + (-1)^2 + (-1)^2 + 5^2 = \underline{\hspace{3cm}}$$

49

36

100. The opposite of squaring a number is taking a square root. The square root of 25 or $\sqrt{25} = 5$; $\sqrt{16} =$ _____.

✻✻✻✻✻✻✻✻✻✻✻✻✻✻✻✻✻✻✻✻✻✻✻✻✻✻✻

4

101. When some arithmetic occurs inside a square-root sign, work the arithmetic before taking the square root.

$\sqrt{1+3} = \sqrt{4} = 2$

$\sqrt{\dfrac{5^2+7}{2}} = \sqrt{\dfrac{32}{2}} = \sqrt{16} =$ _____

$\sqrt{\dfrac{(-3)^2 + (-1)^2 + (-1)^2 + 5^2}{4}} = \sqrt{\dfrac{?}{4}} = \sqrt{?} =$ _____

Note: When we take the square root of a number, both positive and negative roots occur; but we are concerned only with the positive roots.

✻✻✻✻✻✻✻✻✻✻✻✻✻✻✻✻✻✻✻✻✻✻✻✻✻✻✻

4

✻✻✻✻✻✻✻✻✻✻✻✻✻✻✻✻✻✻✻✻✻✻✻✻✻✻✻

$\sqrt{36/4} = \sqrt{9} = 3$

102. Squaring, dividing and taking the square root are used in solving the formula for the standard deviation: S.D. $= \sqrt{\Sigma x^2/N}$. The symbol $\sqrt{}$ directs a person to take the square _____.

✻✻✻✻✻✻✻✻✻✻✻✻✻✻✻✻✻✻✻✻✻✻✻✻✻✻✻

ROOT

44

103. The formula for the standard deviation, $\sqrt{\Sigma x^2/N}$, can be executed in six steps:

1. Compute the mean ($\overline{X}$).
2. Subtract the mean from each score to find the deviations from the mean ($X - \overline{X} = x$).
3. Square each deviation from the mean (x^2).
4. Add the squares of the deviations.(Σx^2).
5. Divide the Σx^2 by the total number of scores ($\Sigma x^2/N$).
6. Take the square root of $\Sigma x^2/N$ ($\sqrt{\Sigma x^2/N}$).

The steps above illustrate why the standard deviation is defined as the square root of the average of the squared deviations from the ―――――――――――.

❋❋❋❋❋❋❋❋❋❋❋❋❋❋❋❋❋❋❋❋❋❋❋❋❋❋❋❋❋❋❋❋❋❋❋❋❋❋

MEAN

104. To see how to calculate a standard deviation, let's assume a distribution of 0, 2, 2, 8. The mean ($\overline{X}$) is 3.

$X - \overline{X}$ or x (deviations) = (0–3), (2–3), (2–3), (8–3)

$\qquad\qquad\qquad\qquad = -3, \quad -1, \quad -1, \quad$ ―――

x^2 (squared deviations) = $\quad 9, \qquad 1, \qquad 1, \quad$ ―――

Σx^2 (sum of squared

$\qquad\qquad$ deviations) = $\quad 9 + 1 + 1 +$ ――, ―――

❋❋❋❋❋❋❋❋❋❋❋❋❋❋❋❋❋❋❋❋❋❋❋❋❋❋❋❋❋❋❋❋❋❋❋❋❋❋

5

❋❋❋❋❋❋❋❋❋❋❋❋❋❋❋❋❋❋❋❋❋❋❋❋❋❋❋❋❋❋❋❋❋❋❋❋❋❋

25

❋❋❋❋❋❋❋❋❋❋❋❋❋❋❋❋❋❋❋❋❋❋❋❋❋❋❋❋❋❋❋❋❋❋❋❋❋❋

25, 36

105. We have found the sum of the squared deviations (Σx^2) to be 36. With an N of 4, the average of the squared deviations from the mean is $\Sigma x^2/N = 36/4 = 9$. The square root of the average of the squared deviations from the mean equals 1 standard deviation. That is, S.D. $= \sqrt{\Sigma x^2/N} = \sqrt{36/4} =$ _____.

❋❋❋❋❋❋❋❋❋❋❋❋❋❋❋❋❋❋❋❋❋❋❋❋❋❋❋❋❋❋❋❋❋❋❋

3

106. Calculate the standard deviation for the distribution 1, 3, 4, 5, 7.
   a. $\overline{X} = 4$
   b. $(X - \overline{X})$ or $x =$ (1–4), (3–_), (_–_), (_ _), (_ _)
   c. $x =$ —, —, —, —, —
   d. $\Sigma x^2 =$ _ + _ + _ + _ + _
   e. $\Sigma x^2/N =$ ____
   f. S.D. $= \sqrt{\Sigma x^2/N} =$ ____.

❋❋❋❋❋❋❋❋❋❋❋❋❋❋❋❋❋❋❋❋❋❋❋❋❋❋❋❋❋❋❋❋❋❋❋

4, (4–4), (5–4), (7–4)

–3, –1, 0, 1, 3

9, 1, 0, 1, 9

4

❋❋❋❋❋❋❋❋❋❋❋❋❋❋❋❋❋❋❋❋❋❋❋❋❋❋❋❋❋❋❋❋❋❋❋

2

107. Subtracting a constant from or adding a constant to all the raw scores of a distribution does not change the value of the stand-

ard deviation. If the standard deviation of 50, 52, 52, 58 is 3, the standard deviation of 50–50, 52–50, 52–50, 58–50 or 0, 2, 2, 8 is _____.

Note: The formula used here for computing standard deviations is based directly on the definition of standard deviation. This formula was chosen because it best helps one understand the basic concept of standard deviation. If you have to calculate standard deviations of various data, consult a statistical methods book for the standard deviation formula most appropriate to your data.

❊❊❊❊❊❊❊❊❊❊❊❊❊❊❊❊❊❊❊❊❊❊❊❊❊❊

3

108. The range is easier to understand and easier to calculate than the standard deviation but it has some serious disadvantages. Not much else can be done with the range. The standard deviation (and its square called the variance) is used in many kinds of statistical analysis. The measure of variation having the greater versatility is the _____.

❊❊❊❊❊❊❊❊❊❊❊❊❊❊❊❊❊❊❊❊❊❊❊❊❊❊

STANDARD DEVIATION

109. The size of the range depends a good deal upon the size of the sample. There is more chance of simultaneously drawing a very high score and a very low score when the sample is larger. Consequently, range generally increases with an increase in the size of the _____.

❊❊❊❊❊❊❊❊❊❊❊❊❊❊❊❊❊❊❊❊❊❊❊❊❊❊

SAMPLE

110. Because all the scores are used in computing the standard deviation while only two scores (the highest and lowest) are used in computing the range, the standard deviation is much more stable than the range. The more stable measure of variability is the _____.

✻✻✻✻✻✻✻✻✻✻✻✻✻✻✻✻✻✻✻✻✻✻✻✻✻✻✻✻✻✻✻✻✻

STANDARD DEVIATION

111. For example, a sample of 20 scores could be drawn at random from a population of 200 scores. The standard deviation and the range could now be calculated and the 20 scores returned to the population pile. If this process were repeated many times, the standard deviations would vary in size much less than would the _____.

✻✻✻✻✻✻✻✻✻✻✻✻✻✻✻✻✻✻✻✻✻✻✻✻✻✻✻✻✻✻✻✻✻

RANGE

INTERPRETING TEST SCORES

112. The number of correct answers that a person acquires on a test is called his raw score. Assuming that each question on a test counted one point, a raw score of 12 would mean that an individual answered _____ questions correctly.

✻✻✻✻✻✻✻✻✻✻✻✻✻✻✻✻✻✻✻✻✻✻✻✻✻✻✻✻✻✻✻✻✻

113. The raw score alone is a poor indicator of test performance. For example, a raw score of 40 points out of a possible total of 40 points suggests good performance. A raw score of 40 points out of a possible 400 suggests poor performance. In both cases 40 points is the _____ _____.

****

RAW SCORE

114. A somewhat better indicator of test performance is the percentage score (number right/total number of questions $\times$ 100). What percentage score does 100 right out of 400 questions receive? _____

****

25%

115. Raw scores or percentage scores do not signify a student's performance *relative to the rest of the group*. A person cannot tell whether a percentage score of 91% is good or bad unless he knows the other students' scores. It is possible that all the other students received scores higher than 91%. In such a case 91% would be a low score _____ to the rest of the group.

****

COMPARED OR RELATIVE

116. If scores are ranked from lowest to highest, we can indicate a person's position relative to the group by stating, for instance, that out of a group of ten, he ranks fourth *from the bottom*. What is the rank of the person with a test score of 91% in the distribution 83%, 85%, 88%, 91%, 96%? _____

FOURTH (FROM THE BOTTOM)

117. While the sizes of the two hypothetical groups in the preceding frame were different (10 and 5), the selected persons had the same _____ .

RANK

118. The person who ranked fourth in a group of ten was not as relatively high as the person who ranked fourth out of a group of five. A rank by itself has little meaning unless the *total number* of persons in the group is known. The weakness of ranks then is that they depend upon the _____ _____ of persons in a group.

NUMBER OR TOTAL NUMBER

119. The disadvantages of raw scores, percentage scores, and ranks are avoided by converting a person's rank to the number of cases he would equal or surpass if there were 100 cases in

the group. Groups of different sizes are more directly comparable by saying what a person's rank would be out of a group of _____.

✸✸✸✸✸✸✸✸✸✸✸✸✸✸✸✸✸✸✸✸✸✸✸✸✸✸✸✸✸✸✸✸✸✸
100

120. The conversion of ranks to a scale of 100 can be exemplified by the following illustration. If the total number of a group (let us say 5) were set to 100, 1 would equal 20 and 5 would equal 100. What would the rank of 4 equal on the scale of 100? _____

Rank: 0   1   2   3   4   5

Rank scaled to 100 units: 0   20   40   60   80   100

✸✸✸✸✸✸✸✸✸✸✸✸✸✸✸✸✸✸✸✸✸✸✸✸✸✸✸✸✸✸✸✸✸✸
80

121. The person with a rank of 4 in a group of 5 is 80% of the way toward the top of the group, i.e., he *equaled* or *surpassed* ⅘ or _____% of the group.

✸✸✸✸✸✸✸✸✸✸✸✸✸✸✸✸✸✸✸✸✸✸✸✸✸✸✸✸✸✸✸✸✸✸
80

122. The person with a rank of 3 in a group of 10 is 30% of the way toward the top of the group. He is surpassed by 7/10 or _____% of the group.

✸✸✸✸✸✸✸✸✸✸✸✸✸✸✸✸✸✸✸✸✸✸✸✸✸✸✸✸✸✸✸✸✸✸
70

123. As he equals or surpasses 30% of the group, if there were 100 persons in the group, he would equal or surpass _____ _____ persons.

※※※※※※※※※※※※※※※※※※※※※※※※※※※※※※※※

30

124. Rank expressed in terms of percentage (meaning per hundred) is called percentile rank. A person with a rank equivalent to being 80th out of 100 would have a percentile rank of _____ _____.

※※※※※※※※※※※※※※※※※※※※※※※※※※※※※※※※

80

125. If a person is 15th from the bottom of his class of 25, he is $^{15}\!/_{25}$ or $^{3}\!/_{5}$ of the way toward the top of the class. He has a percentile rank of 60 and equals or surpasses _____% of his group.

※※※※※※※※※※※※※※※※※※※※※※※※※※※※※※※※

60%

126. In a 30-item test the raw scores 20, 23, 27, and 29, were obtained Notice the relationship of the raw scores to their respective percentage scores, ranks, and percentile ranks in the following illustration. At what percentile rank does the percentage score of 66 lie? _____

Raw score:		20	23	27	29
Percentage score:		66%	77%	90%	97%
Rank:	0	1	2	3	4
Percentile rank:	0	25	50	75	100

※※※※※※※※※※※※※※※※※※※※※※※※※※※※※※※※

25ᴛʜ

127. A percentage grade (or score) sets the total number of test questions to 100 while a percentile rank or score sets the total number of *people* taking the test to _____.

✻✻✻✻✻✻✻✻✻✻✻✻✻✻✻✻✻✻✻✻✻✻✻✻✻✻✻✻✻✻✻✻✻✻

100

128. Percentile ranks can be computed by a simple formula: $PR =$ Rank/$N \times 100$. If a person ranked 8th in a group of 20, he would equal or surpass $\frac{8}{20}$ of the group with a percentile rank of _____.

✻✻✻✻✻✻✻✻✻✻✻✻✻✻✻✻✻✻✻✻✻✻✻✻✻✻✻✻✻✻✻✻✻✻✻✻

40

129. A score with a *PR* of 40 means that 40% of the scores fall *at* or *below* this particular score. What percentage of the scores falls at or below a score that ranks 35th out of 50? _____ What percentage fall above a *PR* of 70? _____

✻✻✻✻✻✻✻✻✻✻✻✻✻✻✻✻✻✻✻✻✻✻✻✻✻✻✻✻✻✻✻✻✻✻✻✻

70%

✻✻✻✻✻✻✻✻✻✻✻✻✻✻✻✻✻✻✻✻✻✻✻✻✻✻✻✻✻✻✻✻✻✻✻✻

30%

130. In the distribution 20, 20, 20, 30, 40, 40, 60 the ranks of 30 and 60 are obviously 4 and 7, respectively, but the ranks of the

tied scores 20 and 40 are less obvious. The ranks occupied by 20 are 1, 2 and 3. The ranks occupied by 40 are _____ _____ and _____.

❊❊❊❊❊❊❊❊❊❊❊❊❊❊❊❊❊❊❊❊❊❊❊❊❊❊❊❊❊

5 AND 6

131. When scores of the same value occupy more than one rank, the mean of those ranks is regarded as the tied-scores rank. For example, the rank of 20, that is, the mean of the ranks 1, 2, and 3, equals 2. The tied score 40, which occupies ranks 5 and 6, has a rank of _____.

❊❊❊❊❊❊❊❊❊❊❊❊❊❊❊❊❊❊❊❊❊❊❊❊❊❊❊❊❊

5.5

132. The ranks for the whole distribution now run as follows:

Raw score:	20,	20,	20,	30,	40,	40,	60
Rank:	2,	2,	2,	4,	5.5,	5.5,	7

Did the calculations for tied ranks affect the ranks of untied scores? _____.

❊❊❊❊❊❊❊❊❊❊❊❊❊❊❊❊❊❊❊❊❊❊❊❊❊❊❊❊❊

NO

133. In the distribution 19, 22, 26, 26, 26, 34, 35 the tied scores of 26 have a rank of 4 and the scores of 34 and 35 have the ranks of _____ and _____, respectively.

❊❊❊❊❊❊❊❊❊❊❊❊❊❊❊❊❊❊❊❊❊❊❊❊❊❊❊❊❊

6 AND 7

134. Since the rank of 26 is treated as 4 and N is 7, the percentile rank of 26 is $\frac{4}{7} \times 100 = 57.14$ or 57. (Percentile ranks are usually rounded to the nearest whole number.) The percentile rank of the score of 34 is _____.

✳✳✳✳✳✳✳✳✳✳✳✳✳✳✳✳✳✳✳✳✳✳✳✳✳✳✳✳✳✳✳✳✳✳

86 (ROUNDED FROM 85.71)

STANDARD SCORE

135. Since raw scores tend to cluster around the mean of a distribution the percentile ranks do not have a constant relationship to the raw scores. From what is present of the following percentile-rank table, would it be possible to predict the omitted raw score? _____

Raw Score	Percentile Rank
10	5
22	10
23	15
28	20
?	25

✳✳✳✳✳✳✳✳✳✳✳✳✳✳✳✳✳✳✳✳✳✳✳✳✳✳✳✳✳✳✳✳✳✳

NO

136. Because percentile ranks do not have a constant relation to their scores it is meaningless to average percentile ranks. Could you properly average the following percentile ranks? 2, 3, 5, 10? _____

✳✳✳✳✳✳✳✳✳✳✳✳✳✳✳✳✳✳✳✳✳✳✳✳✳✳✳✳✳✳✳✳✳✳

NO

137. A measure of relative standing that has a constant relationship to raw scores and that can be legitimately averaged is the *standard score*. Standard scores can be computed for any distribution but their interpretation is difficult if the distribution is not normal. The conclusions of this program are valid only when the distribution is near normal or normal. From what is present of the following table, predict the omitted raw score.

Raw Score	Standard Score
40	−2
45	−1
50	0
55	+1
?	+2

❋❋❋❋❋❋❋❋❋❋❋❋❋❋❋❋❋❋❋❋❋❋❋❋❋❋❋

60

z SCORE

138. A standard score is expressed in units of the standard deviation. It tells us how many standard deviations a score is above or below the mean. A score 2 standard deviations above the mean would have a standard score of +2 while a score 1 standard deviation *below* the mean would have a standard score of

_____.

❋❋❋❋❋❋❋❋❋❋❋❋❋❋❋❋❋❋❋❋❋❋❋❋❋❋❋

−1

139. This type of standard score is called a z score. What is the z score of a person who ranks 3 standard deviations above the mean? _____

❋❋❋❋❋❋❋❋❋❋❋❋❋❋❋❋❋❋❋❋❋❋❋❋❋❋❋❋❋

+3

140. The z score can be computed conveniently by dividing a score's deviation from the mean by the standard deviation $(z = x/\sigma)$. If the mean of a distribution is 70 and the standard deviation is 6, what z score is assigned to the person obtaining a score of 82? _____.

❋❋❋❋❋❋❋❋❋❋❋❋❋❋❋❋❋❋❋❋❋❋❋❋❋❋❋❋❋

$$z = \frac{82 - 70}{6} = +2$$

141. The mean raw score has a z score of _____ and (assuming a symmetrical distribution) would have _____% of the cases lying below it.

❋❋❋❋❋❋❋❋❋❋❋❋❋❋❋❋❋❋❋❋❋❋❋❋❋❋❋❋❋

0 OR ZERO

❋❋❋❋❋❋❋❋❋❋❋❋❋❋❋❋❋❋❋❋❋❋❋❋❋❋❋❋❋

50

142. Because z scores are based on the normal curve, we can deduce the proportion of cases above or below a particular z score. For example, about 34% of the normal curve's area lies between the mean and $+1\sigma$. Therefore, the percentage of cases lying below a z score of $+1$ is 34% plus the 50% of total cases that

lie below the mean. The total percentage of cases lying below
a z score of +1 is _____%.

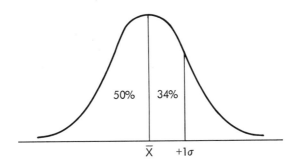

＊＊＊＊＊＊＊＊＊＊＊＊＊＊＊＊＊＊＊＊＊＊＊＊＊＊＊＊＊＊＊＊＊

84% (34% + 50%)

143. A z score usually isn't in whole numbers (as +1 or −2) but
    some fractional value (as +1.37 or −2.81). Most statistical
    methods texts contain a table that gives the area of the curve
    between the mean and a particular z score. From the partial
    table below, give the percentage of cases lying between the
    mean and a z score of +1.96. _____

| | % of Area from Mean |
z Score (x/σ)	to z Score (x/σ)
1.95	47.44
1.96	47.50
1.97	47.56
1.98	47.61
1.99	47.67
2.00	47.72

＊＊＊＊＊＊＊＊＊＊＊＊＊＊＊＊＊＊＊＊＊＊＊＊＊＊＊＊＊＊＊＊＊

47.50%

58

144. If 47.50% of the total cases are between the mean and a z score of +1.96, what percentage of the total cases lies below a z score of + 1.96? _____ What is the percentage of cases above? _____

50% PLUS 47.50% OR 97.50%

2.50%

145. Because the mean of a normal distribution has a z score of zero, any score above the mean has a positive z score and any score below the mean has a _____ z score.

NEGATIVE

146. Sometimes it is desirable to have the advantage of z scores but without decimals and negative numbers. Thus, College Board scores and some other standard test scores are modified from z scores. The formula for College Board scores is $(x/\sigma)\,100 + 500$. That is, multiply the z score (x/σ) by 100 and add _____
_____.

500

147. A z score of −2 becomes a College Board score of −2(100) + 500 = 300; a z score of +1.96 becomes +1.96(100) + 500 = 696; and a z score of +1 becomes _____.

600

148. Since standard scores are based upon the model of the normal curve, they are inept when describing a population whose distribution is not normal. Would standard scores aptly describe

a person's position in a bimodal population? _____
Would percentile ranks be more appropriate? _____

❋❋❋❋❋❋❋❋❋❋❋❋❋❋❋❋❋❋❋❋❋❋❋❋❋❋❋❋❋

NO

❋❋❋❋❋❋❋❋❋❋❋❋❋❋❋❋❋❋❋❋❋❋❋❋❋❋❋❋❋

YES

RELATIONSHIP: CORRELATION COEFFICIENT

149. Many variables or events in nature are related to each other. As the sun rises, the day warms up; as children age, they think more complexly; and persons bright in one area tend to be bright in others. Such relationships are called correlations. The relationship of one variable to another is known as a _____.

❋❋❋❋❋❋❋❋❋❋❋❋❋❋❋❋❋❋❋❋❋❋❋❋❋❋❋❋❋

CORRELATION

150. If the river rises when it rains, the two events are said to have a positive correlation. That is, when an increase in one variable coincides with an increase in another variable, the two variables have a _____ correlation.

❋❋❋❋❋❋❋❋❋❋❋❋❋❋❋❋❋❋❋❋❋❋❋❋❋❋❋❋❋

POSITIVE

151. Altitude and air pressure have a negative correlation. The greater the altitude, the less the air pressure. When an increase in one variable coincides with a decrease in another variable,

the two variables have a negative correlation. With children, bedwetting and age usually have a _____

❊❊❊❊❊❊❊❊❊❊❊❊❊❊❊❊❊❊❊❊❊❊❊❊❊❊❊❊❊❊❊❊❊

NEGATIVE CORRELATION

152. When there is a high correlation between two variables, we can predict the values for one variable from those of the other. If there is a high positive correlation between drownings and ice cream sales we can predict that as ice cream sales increase the number of drownings will _____.

❊❊❊❊❊❊❊❊❊❊❊❊❊❊❊❊❊❊❊❊❊❊❊❊❊❊❊❊❊❊❊❊❊

INCREASE

153. We can predict the occurrence of one event from another event, but we cannot say that one event *causes* the other event. There is a positive correlation between the number of drownings per day and ice cream sales, but drownings do not cause the ice cream sales or vice versa. A third variable, heat, is probably _____ of both events.

❊❊❊❊❊❊❊❊❊❊❊❊❊❊❊❊❊❊❊❊❊❊❊❊❊❊❊❊❊❊❊❊❊

THE CAUSE

154. There must be a common link between the sets of variables being correlated. If two tests are correlated, the same person or persons that are matched on related variables must take both tests. Could one correlate the performance of a fifth-grade class on test A with the performance of another *un-matched* fifth-grade class on test A? _____

❊❊❊❊❊❊❊❊❊❊❊❊❊❊❊❊❊❊❊❊❊❊❊❊❊❊❊❊❊❊❊❊❊

NO

155. The most common numerical measure of correlation is the product moment correlation coefficient. This is commonly symbolized by the small letter r. Whenever we see r, it symbolizes the _____   _____   _____

_____.

Note: We will not be concerned with the calculation of r, but rather with the familiarization of the concept.

❊❊❊❊❊❊❊❊❊❊❊❊❊❊❊❊❊❊❊❊❊❊❊❊❊❊❊❊❊❊❊

PRODUCT MOMENT CORRELATION COEFFICIENT

156. The value r measures the degree to which the relationship between two variables can be represented by a *straight* line. Which of the variables in the diagrams below, X, Y, or Z, has the highest r with the variable A? _____

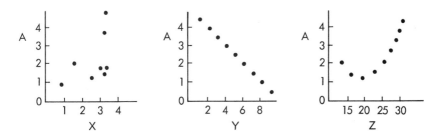

❊❊❊❊❊❊❊❊❊❊❊❊❊❊❊❊❊❊❊❊❊❊❊❊❊❊❊❊❊

Y

157. The value r ranges from $+1.00$ for a perfect positive linear (straight line) relationship, through 0.00 for no linear relationship, to -1.00 for a perfect _____ linear relationship.

❊❊❊❊❊❊❊❊❊❊❊❊❊❊❊❊❊❊❊❊❊❊❊❊❊❊❊❊❊

NEGATIVE

158. We have learned that when high values on one test tend to go with low values on another test the tests are negatively correlated. The algebraic sign of minus (−) indicates a negative correlation or an inverse relationship. The algebraic sign of plus (+) indicates a positive correlation or a direct relationship. Which diagram illustrates inversely related variables having an $r = -1.00$? _____

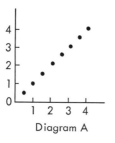 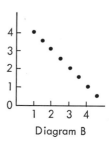

Diagram A   Diagram B

✻✻✻✻✻✻✻✻✻✻✻✻✻✻✻✻✻✻✻✻✻✻✻✻✻✻✻✻✻✻✻✻✻✻

B

159. A correlation of −1.00 is as high a correlation as +1.00. The algebraic sign (+ or −) of the correlation coefficient indicates the direction of the relationship (whether direct or inverse). It is the absolute size of r that indicates the degree of strength or closeness of the relationship. Is an r of −0.80 higher or lower than an r of +0.65? _____

✻✻✻✻✻✻✻✻✻✻✻✻✻✻✻✻✻✻✻✻✻✻✻✻✻✻✻✻✻✻✻✻✻✻

HIGHER

160. In the real world it is more common than not for the value of r to be much lower than −1.00 or +1.00. The closer the dots approach a straight thin line, the higher the r. Which of the

variables (X, Y, or Z) has the highest r with the variable A? _____ Which the lowest? _____

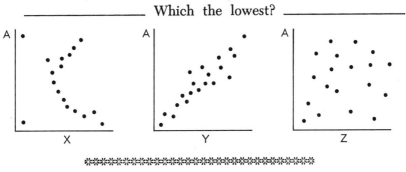

❀❀❀❀❀❀❀❀❀❀❀❀❀❀❀❀❀❀❀❀❀❀❀❀❀❀❀❀❀❀

Y

❀❀❀❀❀❀❀❀❀❀❀❀❀❀❀❀❀❀❀❀❀❀❀❀❀❀❀❀❀❀

Z

161. To get a feel for the closeness of relationship indicated by various sizes of r (all positive for easy comparison), examine the following graphs, and by comparing, estimate the r of Graph E. _____

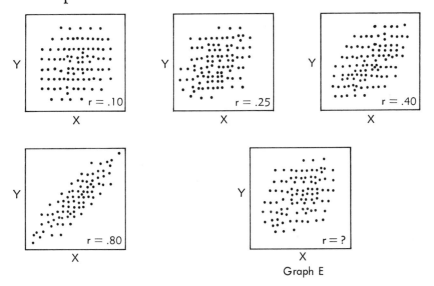

❀❀❀❀❀❀❀❀❀❀❀❀❀❀❀❀❀❀❀❀❀❀❀❀❀❀❀

r = .25

162. A correlation coefficient is not a direct measure of the percentage of relationship between two variables. One cannot say that a correlation of +0.90 is three times as close a relationship as +0.30, but merely that it indicates a much higher degree of relationship. The correlation values or coefficients of correlation are not measurements on a scale of equal units. Are two tests having an r of +0.40 twice as related as two tests having an r of +0.20? _____

❋❋❋❋❋❋❋❋❋❋❋❋❋❋❋❋❋❋❋❋❋❋❋❋❋❋❋❋❋❋

NO

163. If the correlation values are not measurements on a scale of equal units, then an *increase* in correlation, for example, from +0.30 to +0.50, is *not* equal to the same amount of *increase* on another correlation, for example, from +0.60 to +0.80. Each of the two correlations experienced an _____ in the closeness or similarity of the variables they were measuring but not necessarily to the same extent or degree.

❋❋❋❋❋❋❋❋❋❋❋❋❋❋❋❋❋❋❋❋❋❋❋❋❋❋❋❋❋❋

INCREASE

164. Whether a correlation is considered high or not depends on what we are correlating. Some predictions do not have to be very precise to be of important use, so as a result even a small amount of correlation is noteworthy. Ignoring the *use* of a correlation, an over-all "rule of thumb" for judging correlation size is to consider an r of 0.70 to 1.00 (either + or −) as a high correlation and an r of 0.20 to 0.40 as a relatively low correlation. Disregarding use, how would you describe a correlation of .35? _____

❋❋❋❋❋❋❋❋❋❋❋❋❋❋❋❋❋❋❋❋❋❋❋❋❋❋❋❋❋❋

LOW OR RELATIVELY LOW

RELIABILITY AND VALIDITY

165. The statistical analogies in the discussion below are in parentheses.

A rifle placed in a vise might hit the same place consistently:

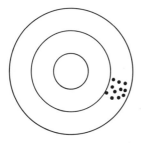

(This is reliability.)

It might in addition be on target:

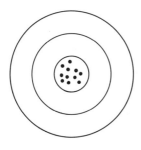

(This is validity.)

Could it be on target (valid) if it wasn't consistent (reliable)?

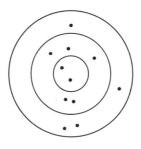

※※※※※※※※※※※※※※※※※※※※※※※※※※※※

NO

166. Reliability is expressed as a correlation coefficient that measures the self-consistency of the test. If any object (instrument, test, experiment, etc.) is reliable, the same results from using the item are obtainable time after time. If one were to use a very crude scale for weighing chemicals, he could not expect his results to be _____.

❀❀❀❀❀❀❀❀❀❀❀❀❀❀❀❀❀❀❀❀❀❀❀❀❀❀❀❀❀❀❀❀❀

RELIABLE

167. The three most common methods of measuring reliability are test-retest, split-half, and equivalent forms. If a test is to give consistent results, it has to be _____.

❀❀❀❀❀❀❀❀❀❀❀❀❀❀❀❀❀❀❀❀❀❀❀❀❀❀❀❀❀❀❀❀❀

RELIABLE

168. Test-retest reliability is established by correlating the scores on the *same test given at two different times.*
In the illustration below, would the form on the right be administered on May 1? _____

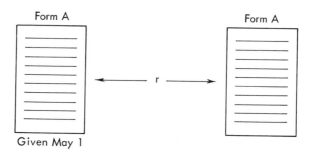

Form A   Form A

     r

Given May 1

❀❀❀❀❀❀❀❀❀❀❀❀❀❀❀❀❀❀❀❀❀❀❀❀❀❀❀❀❀❀❀❀❀

NO

169. Equivalent forms reliability is established by the correlation between *equivalent forms of the same test given at the same time.** In the illustration below, would the form on the right be administered on May 1? _____

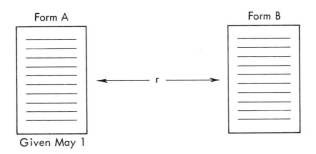

Form A

Form B

r

Given May 1

✽✽✽✽✽✽✽✽✽✽✽✽✽✽✽✽✽✽✽✽✽✽✽✽✽✽✽✽✽✽✽✽✽✽✽✽✽✽✽

YES

170. Split-half reliability is established by correlating the scores on *two halves of the same test given at the same time.*
This type of reliability is most logically related to which of the other two types? _____

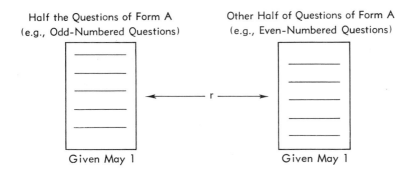

Half the Questions of Form A
(e.g., Odd-Numbered Questions)

Other Half of Questions of Form A
(e.g., Even-Numbered Questions)

r

Given May 1

Given May 1

✽✽✽✽✽✽✽✽✽✽✽✽✽✽✽✽✽✽✽✽✽✽✽✽✽✽✽✽✽✽✽✽✽✽✽✽✽✽

EQUIVALENT FORMS

* Researchers often measure equivalence and stability (test-retest) in combination, by giving equivalent forms at two different times.

171. Validity is expressed as the *extent to which a test measures what it is supposed to measure* (i.e., how well it hits the target). One does not ask if a test is *valid,* but for *what* is it _____?

※※※※※※※※※※※※※※※※※※※※※※※※※※※※

VALID

172. There are four types of validity with which the student should be concerned. They are *predictive, concurrent, content,* and *construct.* Each of these types of validity indicates the test's usefulness for some particular purpose. If we want to know how useful a test is, we have to know how _____ it is for some particular purpose.

※※※※※※※※※※※※※※※※※※※※※※※※※※※※

VALID

173. Validity is the correlation between a test result and some performance called a *criterion.* (This will not be true for content validity.)
The performance against which a test is matched is called the _____.

※※※※※※※※※※※※※※※※※※※※※※※※※※※※

CRITERION

174. A measure of how well a test predicts a person's future job or school performance is called predictive validity. In predictive

validity the performance predicted by the test is the _____ performance.

✻✻✻✻✻✻✻✻✻✻✻✻✻✻✻✻✻✻✻✻✻✻✻✻✻✻✻✻✻

CRITERION OR FUTURE

175. If a test were designed to predict grade averages for incoming freshmen, the criterion would be the actual grade average obtained at the end of the freshman year. The test's efficiency at this task would be called its _____

_____.

✻✻✻✻✻✻✻✻✻✻✻✻✻✻✻✻✻✻✻✻✻✻✻✻✻✻✻✻✻

PREDICTIVE VALIDITY

176. One might be interested in how well a test measured some *current* situation. If high scorers on a leadership test are indeed leaders—as simultaneously determined by judges' ratings—that test could be said to have *concurrent* _____.

✻✻✻✻✻✻✻✻✻✻✻✻✻✻✻✻✻✻✻✻✻✻✻✻✻✻✻✻✻

VALIDITY

177. The only difference between concurrent and predictive validity is time. A test with concurrent validity seeks to estimate *present* performance whereas a test with predictive validity seeks to estimate _____ performance.

✻✻✻✻✻✻✻✻✻✻✻✻✻✻✻✻✻✻✻✻✻✻✻✻✻✻✻✻✻

FUTURE

178. It is easy to understand a third type of validity, construct validity, when one understands the psychological meaning of the word *construct*. A construct ties together a series of related observations. For example, a person might laugh a lot, whistle frequently, speak in resonant tones, and move with unusual vitality. These are all physical observations but if one puts them together and says a person is "happy," one has formed a *construct*. Similarly schizophrenia, generosity, goodness, objectivity, maturity, etc. are not simple acts but are ＿＿＿＿＿＿ derived from a whole set of simple acts.

❋❋❋❋❋❋❋❋❋❋❋❋❋❋❋❋❋❋❋❋❋❋❋❋❋❋❋❋❋❋

CONSTRUCTS

179. The correlation between a test for determining the degree of depression and the clinical observations of simple and discrete acts indicating depression would reflect the test's ＿＿＿＿＿＿ and ＿＿＿＿＿＿＿＿＿ validity.

❋❋❋❋❋❋❋❋❋❋❋❋❋❋❋❋❋❋❋❋❋❋❋❋❋❋❋❋❋❋

CONSTRUCT

❋❋❋❋❋❋❋❋❋❋❋❋❋❋❋❋❋❋❋❋❋❋❋❋❋❋❋❋❋❋

CONCURRENT

180. The synthesis derived from the clinical observations serves as the ＿＿＿＿＿＿＿＿＿.

❋❋❋❋❋❋❋❋❋❋❋❋❋❋❋❋❋❋❋❋❋❋❋❋❋❋❋❋❋❋

CRITERION

181. If a test which was designed to predict those students that would develop *schizophrenia* by their senior year (provided treatment was not sought) correlated very well with *subsequent clinical* findings, one could say that the test had both _____ _____ and _____ validity.

❋❋❋❋❋❋❋❋❋❋❋❋❋❋❋❋❋❋❋❋❋❋❋❋❋❋❋❋❋❋

PREDICTIVE

❋❋❋❋❋❋❋❋❋❋❋❋❋❋❋❋❋❋❋❋❋❋❋❋❋❋❋❋❋❋

CONSTRUCT

182. An examination for a course should reflect the content of the course. The degree to which an examination tests the *content* of a course is called _____ validity.

❋❋❋❋❋❋❋❋❋❋❋❋❋❋❋❋❋❋❋❋❋❋❋❋❋❋❋❋❋❋

CONTENT

183. If the lectures in a course were mostly on French political history but the greatest percentage of exam questions inquired about English economic theory, one could say the examination had low _____ _____.

❋❋❋❋❋❋❋❋❋❋❋❋❋❋❋❋❋❋❋❋❋❋❋❋❋❋❋❋❋❋

CONTENT VALIDITY

184. In order for a test to have a high predictive, concurrent, or construct validity, it must first of all be *reliable*. A test could not be used to predict future performance if the test was not _____.

❋❋❋❋❋❋❋❋❋❋❋❋❋❋❋❋❋❋❋❋❋❋❋❋❋❋❋❋❋❋

RELIABLE

185. From the above it is apparent that reliability can be expressed by a coefficient of correlation representing the relationship between two tests. Validity, however, is expressed by a correlation coefficient representing the relationship between a test and some criterion. The correlation coefficient between a set of measurements and a criterion indicate the degree of _____ _____.

❋❋❋❋❋❋❋❋❋❋❋❋❋❋❋❋❋❋❋❋❋❋❋❋❋❋❋❋❋❋❋

VALIDITY

INFERENTIAL STATISTICS

186. The statistical ideas presented so far are useful for *describing* central tendencies, degree of variability, relative standing, and correlation with data that are available. These are *descriptive* uses of statistics. This branch of statistics is called _____ statistics.

❋❋❋❋❋❋❋❋❋❋❋❋❋❋❋❋❋❋❋❋❋❋❋❋❋❋❋❋❋❋❋

DESCRIPTIVE

187. It is frequently useful to be able to predict the future or know things about unseen persons. The branch of statistics that allows us to do this goes beyond description and *infers* unknown data from known data. Because it is inferential rather than descriptive, it is called _____ _____.

❋❋❋❋❋❋❋❋❋❋❋❋❋❋❋❋❋❋❋❋❋❋❋❋❋❋❋❋❋❋❋

INFERENTIAL STATISTICS

188. A *population*, as used in inferential statistics, is *all* of something about which an inference is to be made. It might be all the senior high school students in the United States, all the wheat in a ship's hold, all high school seniors having I.Q.s of 128, English grades of A and who are female, etc. A *sample* is a portion of some *population*, such as some of the seniors at Centerville High, a bucket of wheat from a ship's hold, etc. It should be much easier to gather data about a _____ than about a _____.

‹‹‹‹‹‹‹‹‹‹‹‹‹‹‹‹‹‹‹‹‹‹‹‹‹‹‹‹‹‹‹‹‹‹‹‹‹‹

SAMPLE

‹‹‹‹‹‹‹‹‹‹‹‹‹‹‹‹‹‹‹‹‹‹‹‹‹‹‹‹‹‹‹‹‹‹‹‹‹‹

POPULATION

189. What is called a population depends upon the researcher's objectives. If he wishes to infer something about the students of Centerville High, the school becomes the population and Mr. Smith's class might be the sample. If we wished to infer something about a bucket of wheat, 100 grains might be the sample and the bucket the _____.

‹‹‹‹‹‹‹‹‹‹‹‹‹‹‹‹‹‹‹‹‹‹‹‹‹‹‹‹‹‹‹‹‹‹‹‹‹‹

POPULATION

190. If the freshman class at a university were measured on some variable, they might be considered by a researcher as a sample of (a) all freshmen ever to attend that university; (b) present freshmen at all universities; (c) men and women around the age of 18; etc.

In general the students may be considered as a _____ of various _____.

❄❄❄❄❄❄❄❄❄❄❄❄❄❄❄❄❄❄❄❄❄❄❄❄❄❄❄❄❄❄❄❄❄❄❄❄

SAMPLE

❄❄❄❄❄❄❄❄❄❄❄❄❄❄❄❄❄❄❄❄❄❄❄❄❄❄❄❄❄❄❄❄❄❄❄❄

POPULATIONS

191. *Sample* and *population* are often used by statisticians to refer, not to people or things, but to data. In this sense, the sample would not be the freshman class at a university but perhaps the SAT scores of these freshmen. The population might be the SAT _____ of all freshmen ever to attend that university.

❄❄❄❄❄❄❄❄❄❄❄❄❄❄❄❄❄❄❄❄❄❄❄❄❄❄❄❄❄❄❄❄❄❄❄❄

SCORES

192. In the same sense, a single test score by a student could be viewed as a sample of all his scores if he were to take the same test an infinite number of times (each time knowing only what he knew the first time he took the test). This hypothetical infinite set of scores would comprise the _____.

❄❄❄❄❄❄❄❄❄❄❄❄❄❄❄❄❄❄❄❄❄❄❄❄❄❄❄❄❄❄❄❄❄❄❄❄

POPULATION

193. The easiest type of sample to understand is the *simple random sample*. (There are other types of valid random samples besides

the simple but their clarification would go beyond the scope of this brief discussion.) For a sample to be a simple random sample, it must be true that any single observation or score of the population (of observations or scores) has the same chance as any other single observation or score (of that population) of being included in the sample and the observations must be independent of each other. Would the heights of all the freshmen at a university in one year be a simple random sample of the heights of all freshmen ever to attend that university?

❋❋❋❋❋❋❋❋❋❋❋❋❋❋❋❋❋❋❋❋❋❋❋❋❋❋❋❋❋❋❋❋

PROBABLY NOT

194. No matter how sophisticated the statistical techniques used, one would be inviting gross error if one presumed test results to be valid for a population of *all* who attempt suicide when one's sample consisted only of those who were unsuccessful. Such a sample is called a biased sample. A sample to be used as representing an entire population must *not be* _____ in regard to that population.

❋❋❋❋❋❋❋❋❋❋❋❋❋❋❋❋❋❋❋❋❋❋❋❋❋❋❋❋❋❋❋❋

BIASED

195. If one tried to predict the results of a presidential election by picking names out of country club member lists and questioning the people selected, one would be working with a(n) _____ sample of the United States population.

❋❋❋❋❋❋❋❋❋❋❋❋❋❋❋❋❋❋❋❋❋❋❋❋❋❋❋❋❋❋❋❋

BIASED

196. A value for a sample, such as a mean or S.D., is called a *statistic*. The corresponding value for a population, such as a mean or σ, is called a *parameter*. In inferential statistics, one uses statistics to estimate _____.

❀❀❀❀❀❀❀❀❀❀❀❀❀❀❀❀❀❀❀❀❀❀❀❀❀❀❀❀❀❀

PARAMETERS

POINT ESTIMATION

197. There are three general kinds of inferences commonly drawn about parameters: *point estimates, confidence intervals,* and *significance tests.* In point estimation we seek the best single value which can be used to estimate a parameter. The best estimate of the mean or median of a population is the mean or median of the sample. If a sample had a mean of 120, the best estimate of the population mean would be _____.
An estimation of a population mean or median based on the sample's mean or median is a point _____.

❀❀❀❀❀❀❀❀❀❀❀❀❀❀❀❀❀❀❀❀❀❀❀❀❀❀❀❀❀❀

120

❀❀❀❀❀❀❀❀❀❀❀❀❀❀❀❀❀❀❀❀❀❀❀❀❀❀❀❀❀❀

ESTIMATE

198. For reasons beyond this brief inquiry into statistics a population standard deviation is estimated by using $n - 1$ instead of n as a divisor. If the sum of squares of *deviations* from the mean for a sample with an n of 5 were 36, the population standard deviation would be estimated at $\sqrt{36/5 - 1}$, or _____.

❀❀❀❀❀❀❀❀❀❀❀❀❀❀❀❀❀❀❀❀❀❀❀❀❀❀❀❀❀❀

3

CONFIDENCE INTERVALS

199. An interval within which a parameter would most probably fall is called a *confidence interval*. (Frames 254 through 263 develop this concept.) If one concluded from a sample that there was a 95% (i.e., 95 out of 100 or 19 out of 20) chance that some population had a mean I.Q. somewhere between 111 and 130, the interval from 111 to 130 would represent the 95% _____ interval.

❋❋❋❋❋❋❋❋❋❋❋❋❋❋❋❋❋❋❋❋❋❋❋❋❋❋❋❋❋❋❋

CONFIDENCE

SIGNIFICANCE TESTING

200. If one were to draw several samples at random from a single population they might very well have different values on some measure (e.g., 5 different 100 grain samples of wheat from a ship's hold might have different mean kernel lengths). Assuming that the samples are unbiased, these sample fluctuations can be attributed to chance. If one were to examine thousands of such samples (and determine the mean kernel length of each sample as well as of the entire shipload), one would find that the means of these samples formed a near normal curve. Most of the means would be clustered very closely to the population

mean. Fewer and fewer means would occur at each gradation of deviation from the population mean, just as in any normal distribution. Even the extreme deviations of the sample means from the population mean are presumably due to ——————.

※※※※※※※※※※※※※※※※※※※※※※※※※※※

CHANCE

201. Although the sample means varied, we know that the population means for all the samples of wheat were identical as they were drawn from the same population. In the behavioral sciences, we usually do not know the population values but can only ——————————— the most likely population values from the sample values.

※※※※※※※※※※※※※※※※※※※※※※※※※※※

INFER

202. Suppose that one were comparing two textbooks for teaching concepts of statistics, say a programmed text and an orthodox text. A sample of students is drawn from a population and each student is randomly assigned to one of two experimental groups. One group would use the programmed text and the other would use the orthodox text. Afterward, their achievement would be measured on the same test. In all likelihood, whether there was a difference in the two textbooks or not, the test scores for the two groups would have different means. Thus, one would wish to know: "Is the difference in test values attributable to a difference in textbooks or to the chance fluctuation of sample means about some common population ——————————— ?"

※※※※※※※※※※※※※※※※※※※※※※※※※※※

MEAN

203. *Significantly different* as in "These means are significantly different," indicates that the two sample means are probably not drawn from a common population (as far as the characteristic being measured goes). If two different methods of teaching yielded achievement score means of 129 and 130 respectively and standard deviations of 10 and 12 respectively, would you estimate that the two samples differed significantly from each other? _____

※※※※※※※※※※※※※※※※※※※※※※※※※

NO

Note: When we say that a correlation between two variables (as determined from a sample) is *significant,* we mean that it is *not* very probable that the sample is a random sample drawn from a population in which two variables have a correlation of zero.

NULL HYPOTHESIS

204. In order to determine whether means are significantly different from each other, statisticians often employ the strategy of testing the hypothesis (called the *null hypothesis*) that these means come from the same population; in other words, they test to see whether the mean differences can be explained as chance fluctuation about a common mean. If a statistical test showed the probability that the sample means are fluctuating about a common mean to be quite low (traditionally below 5 chances in 100 or .05, where .00 means no possibility and 1.00 means absolute or 100% certainty), then one might appropriately reject the _____ hypothesis.

※※※※※※※※※※※※※※※※※※※※※※※※※

NULL

205. To illustrate, consider two matched classes, one receiving teaching method A and the other B. A null hypothesis might be as follows: "The amount of learning achieved by students following method A is the same as or equal to that achieved by students following method B." If the data forced rejection of this hypothesis, one could say that the achievement levels obtained under method A and B differed _____.

✺✺✺✺✺✺✺✺✺✺✺✺✺✺✺✺✺✺✺✺✺✺✺✺✺✺✺✺✺✺

SIGNIFICANTLY

206. Even when the null hypothesis (often symbolized H_0) *is* true, particular pairs of samples would have differences between their means ranging from nothing to quite large values. If a particular experiment yields a pair of means at least as far apart as the 5% most divergent pairs of values expected when the H_0 *is true,* the results are said to be significant at the 5% or .05 level. If an experimenter chose to call pairs significantly different only if they were as divergent as the most extreme 1% of theoretical pairs would be if they were from the same population, he would be working at the _____ _____ _____.

✺✺✺✺✺✺✺✺✺✺✺✺✺✺✺✺✺✺✺✺✺✺✺✺✺✺✺✺✺✺

1% (OR .01) SIGNIFICANCE LEVEL

207. Since the confidence level refers to the maximum chance of rejecting the null hypothesis *when* the null hypothesis is true, an investigator who restricts his investigations to the obvious (such as setting null hypotheses as: men do not differ from women in physical strength, ninth graders do not differ from fifth graders in knowledge of science, there is no relationship between air temperature and ice cream sales, etc.) will almost

always find significant differences and, as the null hypothesis is so rarely true in his experiments, will err much less than 5% of the time in his rejection of the _____ _____.

❊❊❊❊❊❊❊❊❊❊❊❊❊❊❊❊❊❊❊❊❊❊❊❊❊❊❊❊❊

NULL HYPOTHESIS

208. Does using the 5 percent level mean that one will be wrong on the average of 1 out of every 20 rejections of the null hypothesis? _____

❊❊❊❊❊❊❊❊❊❊❊❊❊❊❊❊❊❊❊❊❊❊❊❊❊❊❊❊❊❊❊

NO

209. Since the 5% level is more generous in accepting statements as true than is the 1% level, it is less likely to miss real differences or effects existing in nature. If one didn't particularly mind being wrong when saying a correlation was significant but was very anxious not to miss any relationships that did exist, would it be better to use a 1% level or a 5% level? _____

_____

❊❊❊❊❊❊❊❊❊❊❊❊❊❊❊❊❊❊❊❊❊❊❊❊❊❊❊❊❊❊❊

5% LEVEL

ANALYSIS OF VARIANCE

210. It is common to test to see if the separate means of *several* groups differ significantly from each other. In such an instance *all* the cases in *all* the groups averaged together yield a parameter which is the population _____.

❊❊❊❊❊❊❊❊❊❊❊❊❊❊❊❊❊❊❊❊❊❊❊❊❊❊❊❊❊❊❊

MEAN

211. The technique for making this determination is called *analysis of variance*. Variance is the square of the standard deviation. The variance of a population having a standard deviation of 3 is _____.

❈❈❈❈❈❈❈❈❈❈❈❈❈❈❈❈❈❈❈❈❈❈❈❈❈❈❈❈❈❈❈

9

212. The means from several different groups could have a variance. This would be a measure of variation *between the groups* and is frequently called the *between group* variance. If the variation between the means of the groups was great, we would obtain a large _____ _____ variance. Thus, one takes the group means and derives a variance.

❈❈❈❈❈❈❈❈❈❈❈❈❈❈❈❈❈❈❈❈❈❈❈❈❈❈❈❈❈❈❈

BETWEEN GROUP

213. Each group has a standard deviation (and thus a variance) of its own. The mean of these variances would be a measure of the average variation *within the groups* and could be called the *within-group variance*. If the variation within a group was small, we would obtain a small _____ group variance. Thus, one takes the group variances and derives a mean of the variances.

❈❈❈❈❈❈❈❈❈❈❈❈❈❈❈❈❈❈❈❈❈❈❈❈❈❈❈❈❈❈❈

WITHIN

214. Consider a crowd evenly divided between men and women. This crowd might have a mean height of 65 inches with a

variance of 100 inches. This variance of the total sample could be called the *total* _____.

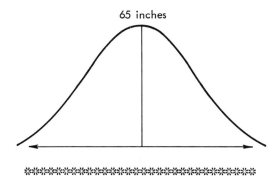

65 inches

VARIANCE

215. Let us say that the men average 70 inches in height and the women 60 inches in height. Taken in total they form the curve below. Its variance is called the _____ variance. What is its mean? _____

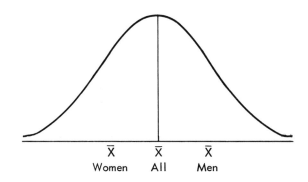

$\overline{X}$ $\overline{X}$ $\overline{X}$
Women   All   Men

TOTAL

65 INCHES

216. Let's say that we now partition this crowd into 2 separate "cells" on the basis of sex.

men	women

The mean around which the men would cluster is now _____ _____ inches and for women it is _____ inches.

✳✳✳✳✳✳✳✳✳✳✳✳✳✳✳✳✳✳✳✳✳✳✳✳✳✳✳✳✳✳✳✳✳✳✳✳✳

70

✳✳✳✳✳✳✳✳✳✳✳✳✳✳✳✳✳✳✳✳✳✳✳✳✳✳✳✳✳✳✳✳✳✳✳✳✳

60

217. If the heights of the men vary less from the mean of men than from the mean of men and women taken together, the variance of men considered separately from women will have a smaller variance than the total variance.

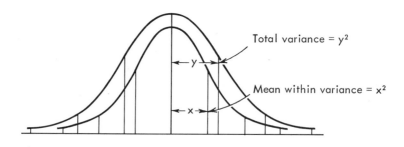

The case would be the same for women. The mean variance of the two groups would thus be _____ than the *total* variance.

✳✳✳✳✳✳✳✳✳✳✳✳✳✳✳✳✳✳✳✳✳✳✳✳✳✳✳✳✳✳✳✳✳✳✳✳✳

SMALLER OR LESS

218. The mean of each of these cells is 60 inches and 70 inches respectively. Since the groups cluster more closely about their new means, their within variances _____.

※※※※※※※※※※※※※※※※※※※※※※※※※※※※※※※

SHRINK OR DECREASE

219. The variance of the *means* (one mean is 60 inches and one mean is 70 inches) of these two groups from the total group mean is 50 inches.

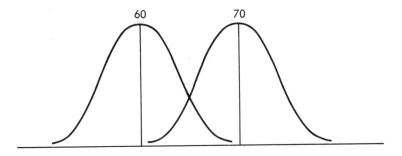

The total mean

↓

$$\frac{(65-60)^2 + (65-70)^2}{(\text{number of groups} - 1) = 1} = \frac{25+25}{1} = 50$$

(Recall that taking the square root of the variance yields the *standard deviation*.) Thus, 50 is the *variance* of the *means* or the _____ variance.

※※※※※※※※※※※※※※※※※※※※※※※※※※※※※※※

BETWEEN

86

220. First, look at the population as a whole:

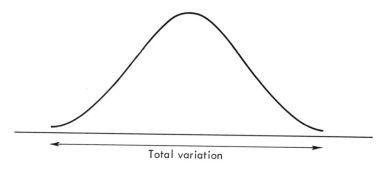

Then look at it split into cells or groups:

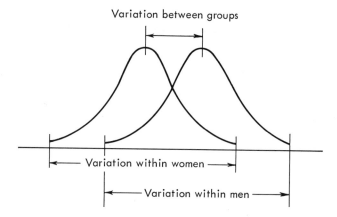

In the case illustrated, the average variation within would be
_____ than the total variation.

❀❀❀❀❀❀❀❀❀❀❀❀❀❀❀❀❀❀❀❀❀❀❀❀❀❀❀❀❀❀❀❀❀❀❀❀❀

LESS OR SMALLER

221. The ratio obtained by *dividing* the between variance by the
within variance is called the F ratio. If the between variance is
6 and the within variance is 2, $F =$ _____.

❀❀❀❀❀❀❀❀❀❀❀❀❀❀❀❀❀❀❀❀❀❀❀❀❀❀❀❀❀❀❀❀❀❀

222. The greater the variation between groups as compared with the variation within groups, the greater will be the size of the _____ ratio.

※※※※※※※※※※※※※※※※※※※※※※※※※※

F

223. Pictured below are two different experiments, one by Dr. Jones and one by Dr. Smith. In each of the experiments the results of three different methods for teaching reading were compared. In both men's experiments the means for the three conditions were 3, 4, and 5, respectively. The results within any one condition varied less in experiment A than B. Despite this, Dr. Smith's experiment showed significant results while Dr. Jones' did not. To see why, note that each of the groups in Dr. Smith's experiment were less variable (and thus his experiment had a smaller within variance) than those in Dr. Jones' experiment. Since the means were the same in each experiment, the *F* ratio (or the *between variance* divided by the *within variance*) would be larger in the experiment by Dr. _____.

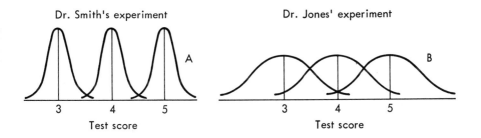

※※※※※※※※※※※※※※※※※※※※※※※※

DR. SMITH

224. The basic question asked in analysis of variance is as follows: "Is the variation between groups enough greater than the variation within groups to make untenable the hypothesis that the groups were samples of a common population?" Would a large F suggest an answer of yes or no? _____

❄❄❄❄❄❄❄❄❄❄❄❄❄❄❄❄❄❄❄❄❄❄❄❄❄❄❄❄❄❄❄❄❄

YES

225. The size of F required for significance varies by the number of groups, the number of people in each group, and the amount of confidence with which the investigator wishes to speak. Would the F required for the .01 level be higher or lower than that for the .05 level? _____

❄❄❄❄❄❄❄❄❄❄❄❄❄❄❄❄❄❄❄❄❄❄❄❄❄❄❄❄❄❄❄❄❄

HIGHER

226. The sizes of F required for significance with particular sample sizes, numbers of groups and confidence levels are to be found in the appendixes of most methods texts on statistics. These sources are appropriately called F *tables*. An F value of unity (1.00) or less is always nonsignificant; thus, if this were the case, it would not be necessary to consult an _____ table.

❄❄❄❄❄❄❄❄❄❄❄❄❄❄❄❄❄❄❄❄❄❄❄❄❄❄❄❄❄❄❄❄❄

F

227. Analysis of variance, then, is useful for determining the significance of difference between *any* number of means. The signifi-

cance of the difference between *two* means is determined by a shortcut that is mathematically identical to analysis of variance and is called the *t* test. Basically, a *t* test would also compare the size of a between variance and a _____ variance.

✻✻✻✻✻✻✻✻✻✻✻✻✻✻✻✻✻✻✻✻✻✻✻✻✻✻✻✻✻✻✻✻

WITHIN

228. *F* tests and *t* tests deal with sample means and are incidentally based on the assumption that the distribution of the variables compared is pretty much normal (i.e., approximates a normal curve). Would it frequently be reasonable to assume that such values as achievement test scores, I.Q.s, heights, weights, etc., would be normally distributed? _____ Would this assumption *always* be correct? _____

✻✻✻✻✻✻✻✻✻✻✻✻✻✻✻✻✻✻✻✻✻✻✻✻✻✻✻✻✻✻✻✻✻✻

YES

✻✻✻✻✻✻✻✻✻✻✻✻✻✻✻✻✻✻✻✻✻✻✻✻✻✻✻✻✻✻✻✻✻✻

NO

229. *F* tests and *t* tests deal with *means* of groups. It is quite a different concept to deal with *expected frequencies*. If one expected that out of 500 tosses of a coin, 250 would be heads and 250 tails, 250 would be called the expected _____ for heads.

✻✻✻✻✻✻✻✻✻✻✻✻✻✻✻✻✻✻✻✻✻✻✻✻✻✻✻✻✻✻✻✻✻✻

FREQUENCY

CHI-SQUARE TEST

230. By the laws of chance, one would expect a tossed coin to turn up heads as often as tails, or a frequency ratio of one head to one tail (expressed as 1:1). Let us suppose that in an actual experiment with a sample of 500 tosses, the frequencies are 270 heads and 230 tails. One might wish to know if these frequencies are compatible with the expected ratio of 1:1. One statistical test that anwers this is the *chi-square test*. While the *F* test deals with measured values, the chi-square test deals with _____ frequencies.

❋❋❋❋❋❋❋❋❋❋❋❋❋❋❋❋❋❋❋❋❋❋❋❋❋❋❋❋❋❋❋❋❋❋❋❋❋❋

EXPECTED

231. If one had an infinitely large population of marbles, for instance, half being white and half being black, and from this population removed many samples of 1000 marbles each, the proportions of black to white would vary widely but would tend to cluster around 500:500 (i.e., 500 white to 500 black). The distribution of sample ratios below shows the distribution of ratios when samples of 1000 are drawn from an infinite population having a frequency ratio of 1:1. What is the most frequent ratio? _____

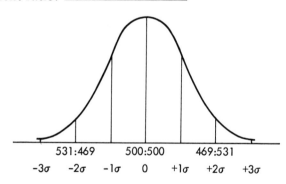

| 531:469 | 500:500 | 469:531 |
| -3σ -2σ -1σ | 0 | $+1\sigma$ $+2\sigma$ $+3\sigma$ |

❋❋❋❋❋❋❋❋❋❋❋❋❋❋❋❋❋❋❋❋❋❋❋❋❋❋❋❋❋❋❋❋❋❋❋❋

500:500

232. Ninety-five percent of the sample ratios would be between 531:469 and 469:531. That is, 95% of the ratios would be closer to 500:500 than 531:469 (or 469:531). (These ratios are calculated from a chi-square table). Ratios in the direction of 500:500 from 531:469 or 469:531 have at least a 95% chance of being from a population of 500:500. A ratio that exceeds these boundaries (such as one of 600:400) is significantly _____ (at the 5% level) from an expected frequency of 500:500.

※※※※※※※※※※※※※※※※※※※※※※※※※※※※※※※※※※
DIFFERENT

233. Any ratio (not just 1:1) is testable with the chi-square technique. Would it be possible to test sample frequencies against a theoretical or expected ratio of 106:100? _____

※※※※※※※※※※※※※※※※※※※※※※※※※※※※※※※※※※
YES

234. A *high* value for chi square (often written as x^2) means that the frequencies probably *differ more* from the expected frequency than is explainable by chance variation. If from previous experience the expected ratio out of 206 live births in a hospital was 106 males to 100 females, which is the most likely ratio one would obtain, 110:96 or 126:80? _____
Which of these two ratios would have the higher chi-square value? _____

※※※※※※※※※※※※※※※※※※※※※※※※※※※※※※※※※
110:96

※※※※※※※※※※※※※※※※※※※※※※※※※※※※※※※※※
126:80

REGRESSION

235. Let us consider the problem of predicting human behavior. In our society this is a common need. Companies wish to predict which of their applicants would become good sales managers. Colleges and universities wish to select those applicants who would profit most if selected for study at their institutions. Prediction is a vital part of modern life.

   Let us suppose that we are trying to predict college freshmen grade point averages (henceforth called freshmen grades) from a paper and pencil test of academic aptitude taken during the senior year of high school (henceforth called the SAT Verbal). For our purposes, let us assume that the r between the SAT Verbal and freshmen grades is $+.50$. Thus, on the average, a person with a relatively high SAT Verbal would tend to earn relatively _____ (high or low) freshmen grades if he went to college with the same group to which he was compared when his relative standing on the SAT Verbal was determined.

HIGH

236. There is an interesting, curious, and fundamental relationship between predictor values and the actions one tries to predict. The predicted actions are more typical (on the average) than the actions used as predictors. Those who have very low values on the predictor will regress toward the mean future performance and thus improve. Those who do unusually well on the predictor also regress toward the mean future performance and thus average _____ (better or worse) in the future performance than on the predictor.

WORSE

237. The principle is quite general. A group of men selected because they are very tall would tend to have sons who, when mature, would be closer to the mean of the general population and thus be shorter than the selected group. Likewise a group of men selected for shortness would tend to have sons who were _____ (shorter or taller) than themselves.

✻✻✻✻✻✻✻✻✻✻✻✻✻✻✻✻✻✻✻✻✻✻✻✻✻✻✻✻✻✻✻✻✻✻

TALLER

238. In the figure below, SAT Verbal scores and grades have been converted to z scores. The mean freshmen grade of all those having an SAT Verbal score of $+2$ is $\dfrac{(+2) + (+1) + (0)}{3} =$

_____.

SAT Verbal z score

✻✻✻✻✻✻✻✻✻✻✻✻✻✻✻✻✻✻✻✻✻✻✻✻✻✻✻✻✻✻✻✻✻✻

+1

239. Because the figure is symmetrical one might suppose that the best match for a $+2$ on the SAT Verbal would be a $+2$ on freshman grades. Instead, the best guess regresses closer to the mean. Fill in the missing values in the following table:

Actual SAT Verbal z score	Best Guess for Freshman Grade z score
+2	+2 times .5 = +1
+1	+._____
0	_____
−1	−1 times .5 = −.5
−2	_____

❀❀❀❀❀❀❀❀❀❀❀❀❀❀❀❀❀❀❀❀❀❀❀❀❀❀❀❀❀❀❀❀❀❀❀❀

+0.5

❀❀❀❀❀❀❀❀❀❀❀❀❀❀❀❀❀❀❀❀❀❀❀❀❀❀❀❀❀❀❀❀❀❀❀❀

0.0

❀❀❀❀❀❀❀❀❀❀❀❀❀❀❀❀❀❀❀❀❀❀❀❀❀❀❀❀❀❀❀❀❀❀❀❀

−1.0

240. Connecting these points yields the following figure:

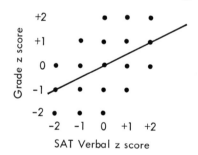

Notice that the line ascends .5 units for every unit it moves to the right. This is called a .5 slope. The line is called a regression line and its *slope* is called a *regression coefficient*. The figure above demonstrates a regression coefficient of _____.

Note: In ordinary practice, the slope of the regression line is not so obvious and is calculated by statistical formulas available in method texts.

❀❀❀❀❀❀❀❀❀❀❀❀❀❀❀❀❀❀❀❀❀❀❀❀❀❀❀❀❀❀❀❀❀❀❀❀

.5

241. If one knew nothing about a possible future student, the best guess of his freshman grade z score would be zero (i.e., the mean for all freshmen). Each S.D. of SAT Verbal allows us to venture another .5 S.D. away from a grade estimate of zero. What would be the best estimate of the freshman grade z score for an applicant with an SAT Verbal z score of $+3$?

_____

※※※※※※※※※※※※※※※※※※※※※※※※※※※※※※※

1.5

242. The general regression formula, when z scores are used is
$\hat{y} = \beta' (z)$, where $\hat{y}$ (read "y hat") is the best guess for the z score variable being predicted
β' (read "beta prime") is the regression coefficient based on z scores (and thus called the *normalized regression coefficient*) and
z is the z score of the predictor variable.
In the preceding frame, $\hat{y} = $ _____, $\beta' = $ _____, and $z = $ _____.

※※※※※※※※※※※※※※※※※※※※※※※※※※※※※※※

$$\hat{y} = 1.5 \quad \beta' = .5 \quad z = 3$$

243. It is interesting to note that the *normalized regression coefficient and r are identical*. Thus, if two tests had an r of .8, for each standard deviation an individual departed from the mean on one test, we could venture to predict that he would move _____ standard deviations away from the mean on the other.

※※※※※※※※※※※※※※※※※※※※※※※※※※※※※※※

.8

244. If the *r* between SAT Verbal and freshman grades were .4 one could best predict that an applicant having an SAT Verbal z score of -2 would have a freshman grade z score of _____.

❋❋❋❋❋❋❋❋❋❋❋❋❋❋❋❋❋❋❋❋❋❋❋❋❋❋❋❋❋

$-.8$

245. Which of the scatter plots below reflects the highest normalized regression coefficient? _____ Which the highest *r*? _____

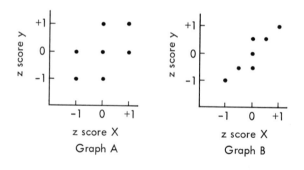

Graph A

Graph B

❋❋❋❋❋❋❋❋❋❋❋❋❋❋❋❋❋❋❋❋❋❋❋❋❋❋❋❋❋

B

❋❋❋❋❋❋❋❋❋❋❋❋❋❋❋❋❋❋❋❋❋❋❋❋❋❋❋❋❋

B

246. Real data would seldom yield a perfectly straight line. The best regression line is mathematically determined so that the sum of the squares of the vertical deviations of the actual data

from the line is at a minimum. Which of the lines below would be the best by this criterion, A or B?

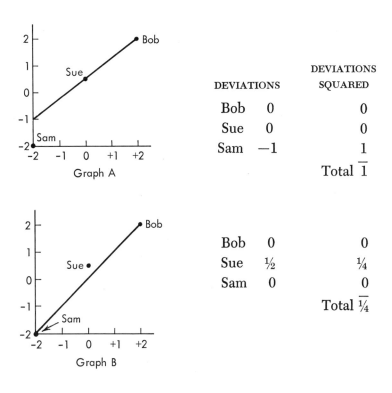

	DEVIATIONS	DEVIATIONS SQUARED
Bob	0	0
Sue	0	0
Sam	−1	1
		Total 1

Bob	0	0
Sue	½	¼
Sam	0	0
		Total ¼

❋❋❋❋❋❋❋❋❋❋❋❋❋❋❋❋❋❋❋❋❋❋❋❋❋❋❋❋❋❋❋❋❋❋

B

247. If a train was 650 miles from a station at zero time (say noon) and going away at the rate of 30 miles an hour, one could tell how far away the train was at any time by using the following formula:

650 + 30 times the number of hours after noon

For example, at 2:00 P.M. the train would be 650 + 30 (2) = _____ miles away.

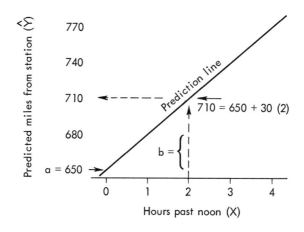

✼✼✼✼✼✼✼✼✼✼✼✼✼✼✼✼✼✼✼✼✼✼✼✼✼✼✼✼✼✼✼✼✼✼

710

248. If the predicted distance is $\widehat{Y}$, the point at which the line cuts the ordinate (650 in this case) is a, the slope (30 in this case) is b, and the predictor variable (time in this case) is X, the general prediction formula would be $\widehat{Y} =$ _____

✼✼✼✼✼✼✼✼✼✼✼✼✼✼✼✼✼✼✼✼✼✼✼✼✼✼✼✼✼✼✼✼✼✼

$$\widehat{Y} = bX + a$$

249. In day to day practice, regression values are usually expressed in the most available units. Assuming, for convenience, a fresh-

man grade mean of 80 for all students with an S.D. of 6, the figure would look like this:

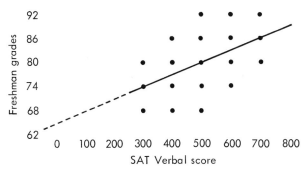

What would be the best grade estimate for an applicant with an SAT Verbal of 700? _____

❊❊❊❊❊❊❊❊❊❊❊❊❊❊❊❊❊❊❊❊❊❊❊❊❊❊❊❊❊❊❊❊❊❊

86

250. Since predicted grades start at 65 and climb 3 grade points for every 100 SAT points (i.e., 0.03 grade points for every SAT point), the best guess for high school grades may be obtained by the following formula:

65 + 0.03 times the SAT score

If a student's SAT score is 200, what specific numbers would go with each symbol?

$\widehat{Y} =$ _____ $a =$ _____ $b =$ _____ $X =$ _____

❊❊❊❊❊❊❊❊❊❊❊❊❊❊❊❊❊❊❊❊❊❊❊❊❊❊❊❊❊❊❊❊❊❊

$\widehat{Y} = $ **71.00**

❊❊❊❊❊❊❊❊❊❊❊❊❊❊❊❊❊❊❊❊❊❊❊❊❊❊❊❊❊❊❊❊❊❊

$a = $ **65.00**

❊❊❊❊❊❊❊❊❊❊❊❊❊❊❊❊❊❊❊❊❊❊❊❊❊❊❊❊❊❊❊❊❊❊

$b = $ **00.03**

❊❊❊❊❊❊❊❊❊❊❊❊❊❊❊❊❊❊❊❊❊❊❊❊❊❊❊❊❊❊❊❊❊❊

$X = $ **200.00**

IOO

251. Note that the value of the ordinate (vertical line) is 65 where the regression line cuts the abscissa (the horizontal axis) 0. From that point, grades soar 3 points for each rise of 100 SAT points (i.e., .03 to 1). One could thus predict any particular case by the following formula:

Predicted grade = 65 + .03 (verbal SAT)

The predicted grade for an applicant with an SAT of 600 is 65 + .03 (600) = 65 + 18 = 83. What is it for an SAT Verbal of 500? _____

80

252. Just as *r* was called *linear* because a straight line was involved, the regression discussed in this program is called *linear regression*. Prediction is usually improved by the fairly complex process of simultaneously using several variables to predict one variable. The technique is called multiple _____ regression.

LINEAR

253. The regression line has a formula which, if known and applied, can be used with varying success to predict anything, once a predictor's relationship to the predicted is known. The equation of the line using raw data involves a constant plus the _____ coefficient times an individual value.

REGRESSION

STANDARD ERROR OF MEASUREMENT

254. Previous experience with this statistics program has no doubt led the reader to the conclusion that an individual test score is a creature about which one can legitimately be skeptical. For example, the law of mean regression discussed in the previous section suggests that high or low instances in a distribution, upon retesting, tend to move toward the _____ of the distribution.

MEAN

255. Because every measurement has some unreliability, one can never be certain that one particular administration of a test, for instance, yields the "true" value or score for that individual. If it's not possible to know the "true" value or score, it's at least good to know how far off we might be. This is possible by the use of the standard error of measurement. Does the standard error of measurement allow us to determine the "true" value or score? _____

NO

256. The concept of standard error of measurement assumes that the "true" value or score for an individual would be the mean of an infinite number of times he took the same test, with the assumption that each time he took the test it was as if he had never taken the test before. Let us be very clear that we are talking all the time here about _____ person taking _____ test _____ (more than

one word) of times. We could list each of one individual's scores and draw a curve to fit this population of his test scores. Let us say he is taking the same I.Q. test a million times. His various scores on this test might yield a curve such as that shown below.

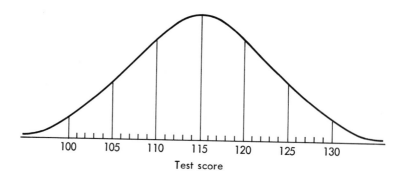

Test score

✻✻✻✻✻✻✻✻✻✻✻✻✻✻✻✻✻✻✻✻✻✻✻✻✻✻✻✻✻✻✻✻✻✻✻✻

ONE

✻✻✻✻✻✻✻✻✻✻✻✻✻✻✻✻✻✻✻✻✻✻✻✻✻✻✻✻✻✻✻✻✻✻✻✻

ONE

✻✻✻✻✻✻✻✻✻✻✻✻✻✻✻✻✻✻✻✻✻✻✻✻✻✻✻✻✻✻✻✻✻✻✻✻

AN INFINITE NUMBER
(OR, LESS RIGOROUSLY, MANY)

257. The same percentages apply here as in the standard deviation discussion. Thus, 68% of this one person's scores on this one test, taken an infinite number of times, would fall within one S.D. of his mean score for all the times he took this one test. What percentage of his scores would fall within 2 S.D. of the

mean (which we may call his "true" score on this particular test)? _____

❊❊❊❊❊❊❊❊❊❊❊❊❊❊❊❊❊❊❊❊❊❊❊❊❊❊❊❊❊❊❊❊

95%

258. The mean, 115, is called his "true" score. Could he ever get 130 on this same test? _____ Could he ever get 100 on this same test? _____

❊❊❊❊❊❊❊❊❊❊❊❊❊❊❊❊❊❊❊❊❊❊❊❊❊❊❊❊❊❊❊❊

YES

❊❊❊❊❊❊❊❊❊❊❊❊❊❊❊❊❊❊❊❊❊❊❊❊❊❊❊❊❊❊❊❊

YES

259. If a person had a Binet I.Q. of 120, and the standard error of the test were 5 I.Q. units, the student might be told that there was a 95% chance (you remember this as the area between -2σ and $+2\sigma$) that his "true" score was between $120 - (2 \times 5) = 110$ and _____.

❊❊❊❊❊❊❊❊❊❊❊❊❊❊❊❊❊❊❊❊❊❊❊❊❊❊❊❊❊❊❊❊

130

260. This particular administration might be one of the dots at the low end of a distribution centered about a "true" value or score of 130 (see A below) or it might be at the high end of a distri-

bution centered about a "true" value or score of 110 (see B below).

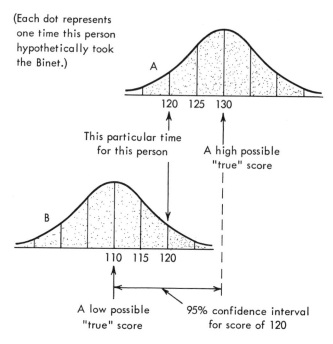

(Each dot represents one time this person hypothetically took the Binet.)

A

120 125 130

This particular time for this person

A high possible "true" score

B

110 115 120

A low possible "true" score

95% confidence interval for score of 120

By using the standard error of the mean, do we know the direction in which the true mean lies? _____

NO

261. If one knows the standard deviation and the reliability coefficient of a test, it is easy to determine its *standard error* of measurement by the following formula: *standard error of measurement = standard deviation $\times \sqrt{1-r}$*. In the preceding equation, *r* is the reliability coffiecient. What is the standard error of measurement for a test with an S.D. of 12 and an internal reliability of .75? _____

262. The band within which one can feel a certain confidence that a score or instance lies is called a confidence interval. The 95% confidence interval of the person with the Binet I.Q. of 120 was thus _____ to _____. Assuming that this standard error was correct, would it be safe (and by safe here is meant only being wrong a maximum of 1 time out of every 20 or 5% of the time) to say that a person with a Binet I.Q. of 130 was brighter than a person with a Binet I.Q. of 119? _____

❊❊❊❊❊❊❊❊❊❊❊❊❊❊❊❊❊❊❊❊❊❊❊❊❊❊❊❊❊❊❊

110

❊❊❊❊❊❊❊❊❊❊❊❊❊❊❊❊❊❊❊❊❊❊❊❊❊❊❊❊❊❊❊

130

❊❊❊❊❊❊❊❊❊❊❊❊❊❊❊❊❊❊❊❊❊❊❊❊❊❊❊❊❊❊❊

NO

263. When one is presented with some individual measurement, such as an SAT score of 450 or an examination grade of 69, one's mind's eye should not visualize a specific point on a continuum as shown below.

But one should visualize, rather, a hazy band. This hazy band typically extends in either direction from the same position. However, the true score may be located in a fairly dense area or in a sparse area. Typically, the true score is in the more dense areas and one can visualize the figure below with the single reported score occurring in the center. The dots representing possible true scores thin out in areas of limited occurrence at the ±3 standard error (S.E.) positions located on appropriate sides of the reported score.

| Occasionally here | Frequently here | | Most often here | | Frequently here | Occasionally here |

S.E.   S.E.   S.E.   S.E.   S.E.   S.E.

One person's reported
score on this test

Hence the standard error of measurement tells one the _____ _____ limits surrounding a given test score. These limits define the space within which a person's "true" score has a given _____ of occurring.

✿✿✿✿✿✿✿✿✿✿✿✿✿✿✿✿✿✿✿✿✿✿✿✿✿✿✿✿✿

CONFIDENCE OR PROBABLE

✿✿✿✿✿✿✿✿✿✿✿✿✿✿✿✿✿✿✿✿✿✿✿✿✿✿✿✿✿

PROBABILITY

Diagnostic Test and Alphabetical Index

INSTRUCTIONS

This test will help you diagnose any weak areas in your understanding of the main statistical concepts discussed in the program. Also, it will serve as an exercise in recall and review.

Work these exercises, checking your answers as you go. (Answers are given on the back of each page.) If you miss any questions and can't figure out the reason for the answers, you will find the appropriate beginning frame number opposite the key index word in the right hand column on the page. Turn to the beginning frame and rework the appropriate section until you are certain that you have mastered the concept.

If you are then still confused, seek assistance from your course instructor.

DIAGNOSTIC TEST	ALPHABETICAL INDEX	INITIAL FRAME
1. Which axis is the abscissa? Y X _____	**Abscissa**	7
2. An analysis of variance could be used to test the significance of differences among _____.	**Analysis of variance**	210
3. Give three measures of central tendency: _____ _____ _____	**Central tendency**	10
4. A chi-square test determines the significance of deviations from expected _____.	**Chi-square test**	230
5. A confidence interval is a range within which a population _____ would most likely fall.	**Confidence interval**	199 259
6. Correlation coefficients may range all the way from _____ to _____.	**Correlation coefficient**	149

ANSWERS

1. X

2. MEANS

3. MEAN, MEDIAN, MODE

4. FREQUENCIES

5. PARAMETER

6. −1.0 TO +1.0

DIAGNOSTIC TEST	ALPHABETICAL INDEX	INITIAL FRAME
7. f is an abbreviation for _____ _____.	f	8
8. A frequency distribution is a _____ of how many times each value occurs.	**Frequency distribution**	1
9. For the distribution 1, 2, 2, 3, 3, 3, 3, 4, 5, draw a frequency polygon.	**Frequency polygon**	5
10. For the distribution 1, 2, 2, 3, 3, 3, 3, 4, 5, draw a histogram.	**Histogram**	6
11. Inferential statistics _____ _____ unknown data from known data.	**Inferential statistics**	186
12. For the distribution 0, 2, 2, 3, 5, 6, give the following: a. Mean _____ b. Median _____ c. Mode _____	**Mean** **Median** **Mode**	11 32 48

ANSWERS

7. FREQUENCY

8. TALLY OR COUNT

9.

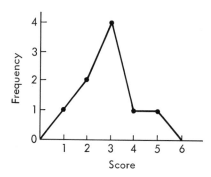

10.

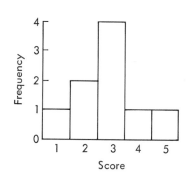

11. INFERS OR ESTIMATES

12.
   a. MEAN = 3
   b. MEDIAN = 2.5
   c. MODE = 2

DIAGNOSTIC TEST	ALPHABETICAL INDEX	INITIAL FRAME
13. What percentage (to the nearest whole percent) of the normal curve area lies within A? _____ Within B? _____ Within C? _____ Standard deviations	Normal curve— areas under the curve	60
14. Check the characteristics of the normal curve. a. _____ Involves small numbers of cases b. _____ Involves large numbers of cases c. _____ Symmetrical d. _____ Asymmetrical e. _____ Asymptotic to base line (abscissa) f. _____ Bell shaped g. _____ Square shaped	Normal curve— definition	60 70 71
15. The null hypothesis states that no population _____ exists.	Null hypothesis	204
16. Which axis is the ordinate?	Ordinate	7

ANSWERS

13.

    A: 68
    B: 95
    C: 100

14.

    b. INVOLVES LARGE NUMBERS OF CASES
    c. SYMMETRICAL
    e. ASYMTOTIC TO BASE LINE (ABSCISSA)
    f. BELL SHAPED

15.   DIFFERENCE

16. Y

DIAGNOSTIC TEST	ALPHABETICAL INDEX	INITIAL FRAME
17. Parameter is used to refer to a _____ value.	**Parameter**	196
18. In the distribution 0, 2, 3, 4, 6, what is the percentile rank of the score 3? _____	**Percentile rank**	120
19. A population is all of something about which an _____ is to be made.	**Population**	186
20. For the distribution 0, 2, 3, 4, 6, give the range. _____ Is it more (or less) stable than the standard deviation? _____ _____	**Range (compared with standard deviation)**	90 108
21. If the correlation between a predictor variable and a future performance is low, the best guess for any particular person's future performance will be _____ _____ (quite near or quite far from) the mean future performance for all persons.	**Regression**	235
22. The most common index of relationship between two variables is the _____.	**Relationship**	149
23. After each of the (three) reliability types below, place two letters indicating which of the following characteristics apply: (a) Given at same time (b) Given at different time (c) Uses same test over (d) Uses similar form of test (e) Uses an internal comparison 1. Test-retest _____ _____ 2. Equivalent forms _____ _____ 3. Split-half _____ _____	**Reliability**	165

ANSWERS

17. POPULATION

18. 60

19. ESTIMATE

20. 6; LESS

21. QUITE NEAR

22. CORRELATION COEFFICIENT

23.
1. b, c
2. a, d (sometimes b)
3. a, e

DIAGNOSTIC TEST	ALPHABETICAL INDEX	INITIAL FRAME
24. A sample is a portion of a _____.	**Sample**	186
25. When one is using the null hypothesis, if a sample difference is believed to reflect a true population _____, the sample difference is said to have significance.	**Significance**	200
26. For the distribution 0, 2, 2, 2, 5, 40, the skewness is _____ (positive or negative).	**Skewness**	15
27. For the distribution 0, 2, 3, 4, 6, give the standard deviation _____. The standard deviation is the square root of the _____.	**Standard deviation**	92 (For background, see frames 71–91)
28. If a person received a score of 120 on a test with a standard error of 5, one could feel 95% confident that his true score lay between _____ and _____.	**Standard error of measurement**	254
29. Facile interpretation of standard scores cannot occur unless the distribution of the population is _____.	**Standard score**	135
30. Statistic may be used to refer to a _____ value.	**Statistic**	196

A N S W E R S

24. POPULATION

25. DIFFERENCE

26. POSITIVE

27. 2; VARIANCE

28. 110 AND 130

29. NORMAL

30. SAMPLE

DIAGNOSTIC TEST	ALPHABETICAL INDEX	INITIAL FRAME
31. Use the numbers below to indicate which of the following types of scores a. Are relative to a group's performance _____ b. Is easiest to obtain _____ c. Is most meaningful when the distribution is normal _____ (1) Raw score (2) Percentile rank (3) Standard score	**Test scores—** **interpretation of**	112
32. Fill in the types of validity expressing a test's ability to do the following: a. Foretell a future event _____ _____ b. Reflect a present situation _____ c. Reflect that which was actually covered in a course _____ _____ d. Accurately label a set of related simple acts _____ _____	**Validity**	165
33. Give two measures of variability a. _____ _____ Which is the most reliable? b. _____	**Variability**	89
34. If the raw scores in a population had a mean of 60 and a standard deviation of 2, a raw score of 58 would have a z score of _____.	*z* **score**	138

ANSWERS

31.
    a. 2, 3
    b. 1
    c. 3

32.
    a. PREDICTIVE
    b. CONCURRENT
    c. CONTENT
    d. CONSTRUCT

33.
    a. RANGE
       STANDARD DEVIATION OR VARIANCE
    b. STANDARD DEVIATION OR VARIANCE

34. -1

Evaluative Data

A basic assumption about programed instruction is that it is equal to or superior to other methods of instruction. The two primary contentions of those who support programs are: (1) the learner is actively involved as he constructs or selects responses and (2) the immediate feedback or reinforcement principle combines to make a meaningful learning experience for the student. Ripple (1963) demonstrated that active involvement is the compelling force in programing, thus suggesting that for a type of material which can be presented either in prose, lecture, or programed form that the programed method is superior. Ripple used 240 Ss randomly assigned to four groups. He used a 50-item criterion test. His method, sample size, and statistical tests are indicative of reliable research. Holland (1960) compared the performance of groups who were exposed to prose, a standard program, and a standard program without feedback. As was the case in Ripple's study, Holland's active involvement and feedback groups did not differ on criterion performance but were superior in performance to those groups receiving the lecture. A series of studies reported by Evans, Glaser and Homme (1959) has been conducted comparing groups taught by programed text materials with groups receiving conventional text presentations. These studies have failed to demonstrate the superiority of programing over conventional text material. Nevertheless, the two methods have proven to be of equal worth. Ripple's study has indicated program superiority over the illustrated lecture.

The studies cited are encouraging enough to warrant further development of programing but each new program should be field tested for both error rate and teaching effectiveness. Properly constructed, programed texts should prove to be of equal or superior merit when compared to other methods of instruction.

Statistical Concepts: A Basic Program was developed for experimental purposes. Its metamorphosis to a complete programed text resulted from the success of an early experiment conducted by Jim Amos with a portion of the present program.

AMOS STUDY

The purpose of the Amos (1963) investigation was to study the relationship between apperceptive orientations and the effectiveness of programed instruction and conventional text preceded by questions. The factors (pedantic and theoretical apperceptive orientation) selected and studied were those factors that could be isolated by the Structured Objective Rorschach Test. The research was designed to discriminate between the criterion test performances of the subjects in the two instructional conditions when the type of test question was considered (knowledge, synthesis).

The sample was composed of 80 general psychology students of various fields of study and grade levels. Forty sets of two students each were identified as high pedantically and high theoretically apperceptive subjects. These sets were matched on previously available stratification variables of: sex, year in school, major field of study, and the College Entrance Examination Board (SAT) verbal percentile ranks. The matched subjects were randomly assigned to one of the two specified instructional methods. There were 20 high pedantics and 20 high theoreticals in each instructional condition. The study utilized sixty-nine frames from the sections on normal probability and variability.

The data were analyzed on the basis of a three dimensional analysis of variance design. The results of the study were as predicted but without significance. The type of criterion test question was the only dimension that differed significantly by sub-levels. All three dimensions showed no significant interaction effects.

The findings of this study suggest that for subjects from a highly selective educational institution, apperceptive orientation and type of test question are not limiting factors. Thus, the program proved of equal worth when compared to optimum conventional instruction.

From this study we were able to draw three conclusions: (1) the program taught effectively; (2) the error rate per frame was low—less than five percent; and (3) students found this method to be an interesting approach to the study of statistics.

OTHER VALIDATION STUDIES

After the Amos study the program was expanded and used experimentally on approximately 100 freshmen and sophomore students studying introductory psychology at Ithaca College. Error rates were checked as well as instructional gains and the results were consistent with the Amos validation. Five separate validation and error rate studies have subsequently been conducted on a program further revised on the basis of the Ithaca College study. The samples involved were: (1) undergraduate educational psychology students at Brigham Young University; (2) undergraduate psychology and education students in two different courses—programed learning and educational psychology—at the University of Toledo, Toledo, Ohio; (3) introductory psychology students at Cornell University; (4) beginning graduate students in guidance at Cornell University. With each of the five sample groups the data indicated error rates of 5 to 7 percent and clearly significant comprehension gains. This edition of the program incorporates all of the needed revisions in frames and frame sequences indicated by these validation studies. Therefore, the finished product represents a more refined program than the one used to gather the statistical data.

The authors have set up a clearing house for additional evaluative data. As you obtain data on the program—error rates, experimental findings, suggestions and criticisms from students or suggested applications—please share the data with us.

REFERENCES

Ahmann, J. S. and M. D. Glock. *Evaluating Pupil Growth.* Boston: Allyn & Bacon, 1959.

Amos, Jimmy Ray. The Relation of Apperceptive Orientation to Effectiveness of Selected Instructional Methods. Unpublished Masters Thesis, Cornell University, September, 1963.

Evans, J., R. Glaser and L. Homme. A Preliminary Investigation of Variation in the Properties of Verbal Learning Sequences of the Teaching Machines Type. Paper read at East. Psychol. Assn., Atlantic City, April, 1959.

Holland, J. Design and Use of a Teaching Machine Program. Paper read at Amer. Psychol. Assn., September, 1960.

Ripple, R. E. Comparison of the Effectiveness of a Programed Text with Three Other Methods of Presentation. *Psychol. Reports,* 1963, 12, 227-237.

Wert, J. E., C. D. Neidt and J. S. Ahmann. *Statistical Methods in Psychology and Education.* New York: Appleton-Century-Crofts, 1954.

Format by Jeanne Ray Juster
Set in Linotype Caledonia
Composed by American Book–Stratford Press
Printed by Murray Printing Company
Bound by American Book–Stratford Press
HARPER & ROW, PUBLISHERS, INCORPORATED